FOOD, SCIENCE, AND THE HUMAN BODY

Alyssa Crittenden, Ph.D.

THE
GREAT
COURSES®

NATIONAL
GEOGRAPHIC™

PUBLISHED BY:

THE GREAT COURSES
Corporate Headquarters
4840 Westfields Boulevard, Suite 500
Chantilly, Virginia 20151-2299
Phone: 1-800-832-2412
Fax: 703-378-3819
www.thegreatcourses.com

MIX
Paper from
responsible sources
FSC® C011935

ALYSSA CRITTENDEN, PH.D.
Associate Professor of Anthropology
University of Nevada, Las Vegas

Alyssa Crittenden is an Associate Professor of Anthropology at the University of Nevada, Las Vegas, where she is also an Adjunct Associate Professor in the School of Medicine. She received her M.A. and Ph.D. in Anthropology from the University of California, San Diego. Dr. Crittenden's focus in anthropology is on behavioral ecology and nutritional anthropology. She does field research among the Hadza hunter-gatherers of Tanzania, East Africa.

Dr. Crittenden's research interests include the evolution of the human diet, the evolution of childhood, and the origins of the division of labor between the sexes. She applies the principles of evolutionary theory to the study of human behavior and cultural diversity. Dr. Crittenden's work crosses several disciplines, including anthropology, psychology, ecology, nutrition, and human biology.

Dr. Crittenden has received multiple awards for her research contributions, including the prestigious Nevada Regents' Rising Researcher Award for 2017. Her research on the role of honey in human evolution and her work on Hadza diet and the gut microbiome have been widely published in both top-tier academic journals and popular outlets, such as *National Geographic* magazine, *Smithsonian* magazine, and *Psychology Today*. Dr. Crittenden has also appeared on the BBC, PBS, and NPR as well as in several documentaries that have been shown in film festivals around the world. ∎

TABLE OF CONTENTS

INTRODUCTION

LECTURE GUIDES

TABLE OF CONTENTS

TABLE OF CONTENTS

TABLE OF CONTENTS

SUPPLEMENTAL MATERIAL

DISCLAIMER

This series of lectures is intended to convey general health and nutritional information and is for educational purposes only. It is not a substitute for, nor does it replace, professional medical advice, diagnosis, or treatment of health conditions. Please consult your physician or other health-care professional before beginning or changing any medical or nutrition program to make sure that it is appropriate for your needs. ■

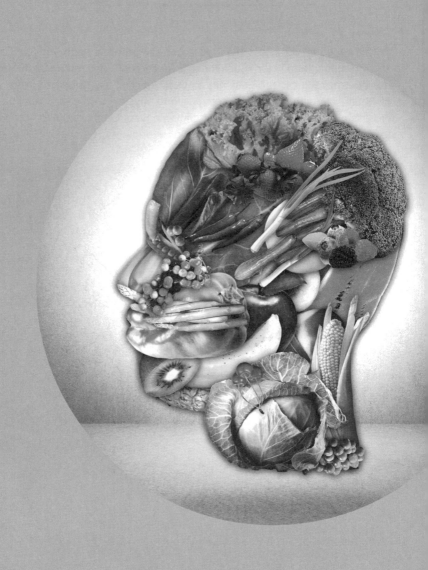

SCOPE

What we eat is central to our daily lives—now, as well as in our past. People have always been intricately tethered to the food that they eat. Subsistence has been linked with not only watershed moments in human evolution, such as brain expansion and cooperation, but also pivotal points in world history. Increasingly, we are learning that what we eat affects our bodies, in both positive and negative ways, and is linked with our health, culture, identity, and even our genes. In this broad-sweeping course, The Great Courses has partnered with National Geographic to provide a look at the history and biology of human nutrition, from the Paleolithic period to the 21st century.

The course begins with an examination of what was really on the prehistoric dinner plate, starting with a discussion of how the Paleo diet differs from the actual diet consumed during the Paleolithic period. The basics of anatomy and digestion are then presented to explore the links between gut physiology, diet, and the evolution of our characteristic large brains. We'll turn to data from the fossil record, stone tools, skeletal anatomy and dentition, and the diets of living hunters and gatherers to inform our understanding of the ancestral appetite. Armed with these multiple lines of evidence, we will be ready to tackle one of the most pressing questions in the study of the evolution of the human diet: Were our ancestors primarily meat eaters or plant eaters?

We then follow the history of humans and their food to the Neolithic period, when our ancestors first began domesticating plants and animals. This was a critical shift in the evolution of our species and involved much more than simply changing food-producing techniques. It was also the time when, thanks to new surpluses in food, we had a huge population boom. Agriculture is associated with many hallmarks of human evolution, such as the development of economies of scale, the division of labor, social hierarchy, art, and architecture. Along with these changes, there were also consequences in terms of our health and patterns of disease. There were also significant changes in the ways in which foods were traded.

With the advent of large-scale trade starting in the 13th century, new foods were disseminated throughout the world, changing the history of human cuisine forever. We'll explore the roles that sugar, salt, and spices play and discover the antiquity and global importance of these powders, plants, and granules. Other consumables have also left their mark on world history. Foods such as bread and chocolate and drinks such as beer, mead, wine, coffee, and soda have been key players in culture, cuisine, religion, economy, and even medicinal treatments around the world.

After the rich historical overview, we'll look at the ways in which food is associated with rituals, holidays, and cultural identity, highlighting the different foods that people eat, including unusual appetites for things that are not considered to be food at all. We'll also look at the fascinating ways in which foods have been used as recreational drugs and medicine.

What we eat is also associated with our health, both now and in the past. Data on the relationship between diet and the brain will be presented, as well as the ways in which food has acted as a powerful force in evolution. We'll review exciting findings from research on the gut microbiome and patterns of contemporary disease and discover what biology tells us about the health effects of a diet based on meat or plants.

The course ends with a thorough examination of food wars and the politics of the production of food. As we look ahead to the future with a rapidly expanding global population, we will need to feed almost 10 billion people by 2050, making the question of what to eat a critical dilemma. The foods that we choose to eat—as a species—will have great implications for the health of the planet and its inhabitants. ∎

PALEO DIETS AND THE ANCESTRAL APPETITE

Figuring out what our ancestral diet is has become a wildly popular topic in the last several decades. This course will pull from many disciplines—including nutrition, ecology, evolutionary biology, anatomy, reproduction, ethnography, history, neurology, psychology, sociology, genetics, and microbiology—to tell the story of humans and food. You will explore what was on the prehistoric dinner plate and then trace the biological and cultural history of humanity's complex, coevolving, and ever-changing relationship with what we eat.

Our Ancestral Diet

- Do humans have an ancestral appetite? Do we have a natural or inherent preference for certain foods? If we do, is this the so-called Paleo diet—the one that we hear about in the media so often?

- Many people are under the misconception that the Paleo diet mimics the actual diet during the Paleolithic period and that we need to get back to our Paleolithic baseline.

- The Paleo diet has been around since the 1970s. It started out as an actual diet and increasingly became a lifestyle and fitness regimen, and it eventually morphed into the Paleo craze that we see today.

- There are many hundreds of iterations of the Paleo diet, with many different guidelines, menus, blogs, and nutrition pamphlets. In its original form, however, it was based on Loren Cordain's *Paleo Diet*, which outlines the foods that people are supposed to eat that are most similar to the diet of our ancestors.

- The idea behind Dr. Cordain's original idea is that our bodies were evolved to eat certain types of food and have not yet caught up with our modern lives—including our diet. In the original iteration of the diet, the basic guidelines were as follows:

  - We were told to eat grass-produced meats. Wild grazing animals eat grass—not corn or grain, like the domesticated cattle that most of us eat.

  - Fish and other seafood were recommended, because they're high in omega-3 fatty acids.

  - Fruits and vegetables were on the list, because the bulk of the Paleolithic diet likely came from plant foods.

  - Eggs, nuts, and seeds were recommended as good alternative sources of protein.

  - Healthy oils, such as olive, walnut, flaxseed, macadamia, avocado, and coconut oils, were recommended because they're healthy sources of fat.

  - We were originally told not to eat cereal grains, which were not available until 10,000 years ago, with the advent of agriculture.

  - We were also warned off of legumes, which the author argues have antinutrients that inhibit digestion.

  - The diet told us to avoid dairy and refined sugar, as they were also not available before the domestication of plants and animals.

  - We even had to watch out for potatoes. Because they're a carbohydrate, they have a high glycemic index, which means a high sugar value food that is readily absorbed by your body, which is assumed to be unhealthy.

- Processed foods, salt, and refined vegetable oils were verboten, because those items were not available in the Paleolithic period.

- There are so many different versions of the Paleo diet now that it can become almost impossible to adhere to all of the guidelines. Because of conflicting recommendations, not only can it become very difficult to determine what to eat if you are attempting try a Paleo diet, but it also becomes almost impossible to figure out what food, if any, was similar to the foods that our ancestors ate during the Paleolithic period.

- Many of the contemporary dietary recommendations are not based on what we actually know the Paleolithic diet was likely composed of. The Paleo diet movement is loosely based on the estimated diet of our ancestors, but there are several key differences.

- We now know that Paleolithic foods would have likely included a wide variety of plant foods, which varied by region and season. These would include fruits from various trees, legumes, and, in some areas, wild barley. Many of the plant foods consumed by our ancestors were also likely high in fiber content—much higher than the plants we consume today.

- True Paleolithic food also meant meat from a wide variety of animals as well as birds and insects. If our ancestors were living in coastal environments, then their diet most certainly included fish and shellfish.

- Just how much they ate is up for debate. But the bulk of the Paleolithic diet was most likely plant based and supplemented with meat. Our Paleolithic ancestors also ate nuts and seeds, which are found in almost every environment and are very rich in fats.

- We also know that many of these key shifts in diet occurred during the Pliocene epoch, which extended between 5.3 and 2.5 million years before the present, and these dietary shifts mapped onto ecological changes.

- During the Pliocene epoch, there were sizeable climatic cooling and drying trends that led to the expansion of grasslands, which in turn led to the expansion of grass-eating ungulates, or hoofed mammals, similar to antelope species today.

- These climatic shifts also meant that early members of our genus *Homo* now had access to new resources, both plant and animal. This dietary shift to higher-quality food sources was also accompanied by physiological and metabolic changes.

- Many of the key anatomical changes associated with this dietary shift are found in gut morphology and brain size and structure. These changes in digestive anatomy likely affected the development of the human brain.

The Evolution of Human Nutrition

- Humans are considered omnivores, eating a diet that has both plant and animal components. It turns out that most mammals are omnivorous. But to understand how humans are different, we first must examine the ways in which we're similar to other mammals—most importantly, apes.

- Apes are our closest living relatives. We didn't evolve from apes; rather, we share a common ancestor with our closest African ape relatives in the genus *Pan*. There are 2 species in this genus: the chimpanzee and the bonobo. We shared a common ancestor with them about 6 to 7 million years ago. We share 99% of our DNA with chimpanzees and bonobos.

- While it's important to pay attention to the ways in which we are similar to apes, it's also important to pay attention to how we're different. That small portion of DNA is responsible for big changes.

But to first figure out what foods might have been deep in our evolutionary history, we have to focus on what our shared ancestor with apes may have been eating.

- All living apes, including humans, share a common plant-eating ancestor in our evolutionary history, and therefore we also share similarities in diet composition and digestive anatomy. We also share a similar gut morphology, or anatomy, with all other living apes. The gastrointestinal (GI) tract is an organ system that's responsible for consuming and digesting food, absorbing nutrients, and eliminating waste.

- The upper GI tract includes the mouth, pharynx (or throat), esophagus, stomach, and duodenum (the first part of the small

Lecture 1 · **Paleo Diets and the Ancestral Appetite**

intestine). The lower GI tract includes most of the small intestine (the remaining sections, called the jejunum and ileum) and the large intestine (or colon), which includes the cecum, colon, rectum, and anus.

- Anatomically, the term "gut" typically refers to the section of the GI tract that extends from the stomach to the anus.

- Most people think that our stomach is largely responsible for digestion, but the stomach is mostly in charge of breaking up food—churning it up and mixing it with gastric juices so that the small intestine can do its job.

- The small intestine is responsible for most of what is called chemical digestion, breaking down the food remnants with enzymes and absorbing the nutrients so they can be taken up in the bloodstream.

- The human gut is similar to that of apes in that we share structures such as the small intestine, stomach, cecum, appendix, and colon. Despite these overall similarities, there are a few fundamental differences that separate the human gut from that of other living primates.

- These include a reduction in the size of the colon and the overall size of the gut and an enlargement of the small intestine. There's a link between the size and shape of an animal's GI tract and what it eats. These changes suggest that our species is adapted to eat a diet of highly nutritious foods that are easy to digest.

- There is also a link between diet and relative brain size. During the evolution of our genus, brain size dramatically increased. From approximately 2 million years ago to today, brain volume has greatly increased, and many scientists argue that it has tripled.

- The relatively large size of the human brain, however, cannot be accounted for merely by an increase in body size, as many of our ancestors were similar in body size to us but had smaller brains. The impetus for such neural expansion is a topic of hot debate among anthropologists and neurobiologists.

- The brain is a metabolically expensive organ. It requires more than 20 times the amount of metabolic energy as an equally sized piece of muscle. While it is only roughly 2% of your body's weight, it consumes 20% of your oxygen and gets 20% of your blood flow.

- This means that big brains are very costly in terms of energy. In the mid-1990s, anthropologists Leslie Aiello and Peter Wheeler proposed that the increase in brain size that we see in human evolution was balanced by a nearly equivalent reduction in the size of the GI tract.

- In other words, they argued that the increased metabolic demands of a large brain were compensated for by the reduction in the energy demands of a smaller gut. A smaller gut meant that our ancestors didn't have to spend so much energy digesting highly fibrous plant foods. And they could devote some of that extra energy to growing a larger brain.

- Despite some recent data that challenges some aspects of this claim, this so-called expensive tissue hypothesis remains a seminal contribution of evolutionary anthropology and is a widely accepted interpretation of diet as a significant aspect of brain evolution.

- Many researchers have linked the aforementioned anatomical changes with increased meat consumption during the Paleolithic period. We know that our ancestors started eating meat, which is highly nutritious and a good source of fat and protein. Meat would have likely been important for growing and maintaining large brains. But they needed other foods, too. And they were probably able to get foods other than meat in a greater supply.

- While everyone can agree that meat was a big nutritional milestone in human evolution, there's a considerable amount of debate in the scientific community over the quantity of meat eaten by our ancestors and what other foods may have made us human.

- Finding connections between diet and behavior can tell us quite a bit about the life and biology of early members of our genus. This, in turn, can tell us whether we may be better adapted to certain diets.

- Some researchers argue that meat is the proverbial smoking-gun food in human evolution, while others contend that all primates, including humans, adapted to a broad plant-based diet that includes only a modest amount of animal protein.

- While the amount of meat in our ancestral diet is still debated, we do know that as our ancestors began to incorporate more animal products, such as meat and marrow, into their diets, a neural expansion took place. This expansion also mapped onto an expansion and refinement of stone tools.

- The refinement of stone tools, in turn, drastically improved hunting abilities. Despite all of this, we still don't know how much meat was consumed. We are also far from wholly understanding the quite significant role that plant foods played in jump-starting neural expansion during human evolution.

Suggested Reading

Eaton, Shostak, and Konner, *The Paleolithic Prescription*.

Questions

1. How is the Paleo diet different from the Paleolithic diet that scientists have estimated?

2. What does it mean to be an omnivore, and how is this our legacy?

OUR HUNTER-GATHERER PAST

For the bulk of human history, our ancestors were hunters and gatherers, also known as foragers, which are groups of people who collect the majority of their diet from wild foods and essentially live off of the land. Scientists, and often the media, consider the diets of foraging populations to be the basis for the evolution of human nutrition and representative of the Paleolithic diet. Hunter-gatherers are by no means models of Paleolithic populations, but we can use data on their diet and lifestyle to test some assumptions about the evolution of human diet.

Who Are Hunter-Gatherers?

- Most people define hunters and gatherers, or foragers, almost completely by the composition of their diet. Anthropologists use what is called their mode of subsistence, which is basically just the ways in which they acquire their food. This is seen as one of their most notable traits.

- In the most austere definition, they don't tend crops or herd animals, and the bulk of their diet comes from wild foods—both plant and animal. These foods can include plants, game meat, fish, and insects.

- Most of the world's hunting-and-gathering populations now practice what is called mixed subsistence, meaning that they eat a diet that includes varying degrees of wild foods mixed with agricultural products. They might grow their own food, trade with agricultural neighbors, or even receive food subsidies from governments and aid organizations.

- The idea that there are still lost tribes in the world who are subsisting on only wild foods isn't supported by any data. In 1966, anthropologists Richard Lee and Irv DeVore led a workshop on the state of the world's foragers, called "Man the Hunter."

- At that time, it was estimated that the world's existing foraging populations represented less than 0.001% of the world's population. In the mid-1990s, it was then estimated that of the few remaining hunting-and-gathering groups, no population was consuming an entirely "wild" diet.

- This is what led author and anthropologist Robert Kelly to propose that the criterion for categorizing a foraging population based on diet composition should mean that approximately 10% to 15% of the diet came from domesticated foods. Using this as a baseline, no populations would meet the criteria in the 21st century.

- There are other criteria that researchers may use—beyond diet— to classify a population as hunter-gatherers. One of them is their unique social life, which includes a high degree of mobility, where they move around the environment in search of resources.

- Some researchers think that foragers should be categorized based on their kinship systems, or the way in which they organize their familial relationships. And some believe that foragers can be defined based on whether their food economy is generalized, or immediate return, versus complex, or delayed return.

- Immediate-return foragers consume their yield shortly after they have collected it, and delayed-return foragers store their food for varying lengths of time. And these are just a few definitions; many more abound.

- All of these categorizations are important, because they provide a snapshot of how difficult it is to bin populations based largely on what they eat. It's also important because most people, particularly those interested in learning about the evolution of human nutrition, are not aware of what a hunter-gatherer really is.

- Despite a lot of media attention when a heretofore unseen group emerges out of the rainforest, the reality is that these populations are rarely eating a predominantly wild diet and almost certainly not uncontacted. Rather, they have achieved their present-day situations out of sustained interaction with other groups—in some instances for at least 100 years.

- This history is important and relevant to the discussion of what we evolved to eat. This is because foragers are still used as referential models of our Paleolithic diet for a few important reasons. More than ever, as their populations dwindle, these small groups are receiving a renewed time in the media and scientific spotlight. Knowing what the limitations are, and how to interpret dietary data from foragers, is important to appreciating what they can tell us about human nutrition.

- We have good historic data from foragers all around the world. For those populations who are no longer foraging, we know what they were eating when they were. For these groups, much of the ethnographic data was collected at or before the turn of the 20th century.

- These data are important, now more than ever, because they can help us ascertain what foragers eat in different ecosystems and how they stay healthy year-round with a limited diet. We can also learn if a wild diet can really provide what our species needs nutritionally.

- We were all once foragers. We all descend from foraging populations. And it wasn't until approximately 10,000 years ago that our lifestyle changed. With the advent of agriculture, our species shifted from being nomadic hunter-gatherers to mixed-subsistence farmers and horticulturalists who ate domesticated plants and animals.

- This is one of the reasons why early scientists have been so keen on researching foraging diet for more than the past 100 years.

During the 19th century, foragers were considered to represent our "primitive" state—language no longer used by anthropologists or other scientists, because it is not only offensive but also inaccurate.

- This language was used because the general consensus was that they lived a life like the one Thomas Hobbes famously dubbed as "nasty, brutish, and short." But this notion is inaccurate.

- These notions persisted, even at the turn of the 20th century. And by the time the 21st century rolled around, the number of foraging populations had plummeted to less than a dozen. This would be the number we would use if we define hunter-gatherers as individuals who obtain the majority of their food from wild resources.

- Modern-day foragers call almost all ecological settings home. Foragers can be found in arctic regions or coastal settings, or both. Foragers can also be found living in rainforests, savannas, mountains, and deserts—in high altitudes and low altitudes. Humans have successfully managed to live and thrive in even the most extreme settings.

- There is as much cultural variation as there is ecological and climatic variation. Not all foragers are the same. Their identities are informed by different customs, rituals, beliefs, clothing, art, material objects, child-rearing practices, family formation, and foodways (the range of foraging techniques that foragers use and the foods that they exploit).

- Given such a wide range of ecologies exploited by foragers, great variation in terms of overall diet composition exists between populations. So, it is very safe to say that there is, and was, not just one paleo diet, but many.

- While the specific foods and the foraging techniques used might vary around the world, there are some basic generalizations. All hunting-and-gathering groups in the world, for example, process their food—whether through fermentation, germination, mechanical processing, dehydration, or thermal treatment.

- There are also some general traits of how much plant material might make up the diet, depending on where in the world foragers live. Some have suggested that the closer a group lives to the equator, with a higher temperature, the more it depends on a broadly plant-based diet, supplemented with meat. And the lower the temperature, the more the group depends on fishing.

- In tundra regions—the coldest of all of the biomes, characterized by permafrost, low temperatures, and short growing seasons—plant foods contribute only a modest 6% to 15% of the diet, whereas the remainder is provided by both marine and terrestrial animal meat.

- The dietary data we have for arctic foragers suggests that, unlike their neighbors from more temperate climates, they consume a majority of meat. This is likely due to the fact that they are able to harvest marine resources more readily in the winter months.

- There is a burgeoning literature, however, that suggests that we may have overlooked critical plant resources in some of our historical reconstructions of diet. As we continue to collect data from present-day arctic foragers, we get a better handle on what these plant foods might have included, such as different species of berries or even kelp.

- On the other hand, temperate climate foragers, such as those who live in the subtropical areas of Africa and South America, eat a diet that is largely composed of plant foods, ranging from 40% to 60% of the diet, with much less meat than previously thought.

The Hadza

- One of Africa's last foraging populations is the Hadza, who live in northern Tanzania in an area of East Africa that is often considered to be the crucible of human evolution. The Hadza have been found to have some of the oldest mitochondrial DNA (passed from mother to child almost unchanged) ever tested.

- In addition, a portion of the population is still foraging for the majority of their diet. Of their total population, which numbers approximately 1000 people, around 250 of them practice a largely hunting-and-gathering way of life. This means that the bulk of their diet is still derived from wild plant foods and game animals. They still wake up every day and have to locate and process at least a large portion of what they feed their families.

- The Hadza are not a Stone Age population; they're just as modern as we are. But they live a nomadic lifestyle in the absence of agriculture or permanent dwellings.

- It turns out that the diet of the foraging Hadza is incredibly well balanced. It's highly seasonal and includes plant foods (such as fruits and greens), nuts, seeds, legumes, honey, and meat from a wide variety of animals.

- While meat remains an important part of the hunter-gatherer diet, it's not the main component. And the meat that foragers are consuming is very different from the meat that the majority of the world consumes.

- People who live in the postindustrialized West, in places such as the United States and Europe, tend to consume commercially produced meat—meat that is far removed, in both time and space, from where the animal lived. While this is changing now, the vast majority of meat that we tend to eat is produced in large industrial settings.

- And much of the meat that we eat is from grain-fed animals. What an animal eats can have a profound impact on the nutritive qualities of the meat that it produces. Much of the meat that's consumed by contemporary foragers comes from small- to medium-sized game animals and birds. The Hadza routinely target small antelope species, monkeys, and hyrax.

- If we were to base our image of the Stone Age hunter on Hadza hunters, we would place much less emphasis on big-game meat. We do know, however, that our ancestors did indeed target and consume large animals, known as megafauna, which would have included mammoths.

- In addition to telling us something about animal foods in human evolution, the types of plant foods that the Hadza consume are also a really important part of the story. For example, baobab fruit and marula nuts are dominant foods in the Hadza diet.

- The baobab tree is a thing of legend. Many groups in the low-lying areas of Australia and East Africa (where the species is found) have creation myths that involve the baobab. The fruit produced by the tree is oval shaped and has an inedible hard green outer shell, but the inside of the seeds contains protein and fat.

- Another example is that of the marula fruit. The Hadza consume the fruit as well as the inside seed of the marula, which we refer to as a nut. They are in the same plant family as the mango, cashew, and pistachio. The fruits are succulent and tart—and fairly high in vitamin C. The inner nut, however, is high in fat and protein. The Hadza consume both the fruit and the seed.

- Despite the constant emphasis being placed on meat and marrow, it turns out that, outside of arctic regions, no contemporary foragers consume a diet that is primarily composed of meat. While meat is important—and it certainly was an important part of our ancestral diet—plant foods are increasingly taking over the spotlight.

Suggested Reading

Gibbons, "The Evolution of Diet."
Kelly, *The Lifeways of Hunter-Gatherers*.
Marlowe, *The Hadza*.

Questions

1. Why is data from contemporary hunting-and-gathering populations important to modeling ancestral diet?

2. What evidence do scientists use to determine whether the diet of subtropical foragers is characterized by a mostly meat diet or a mostly plant diet?

STONES, BONES, AND TEETH

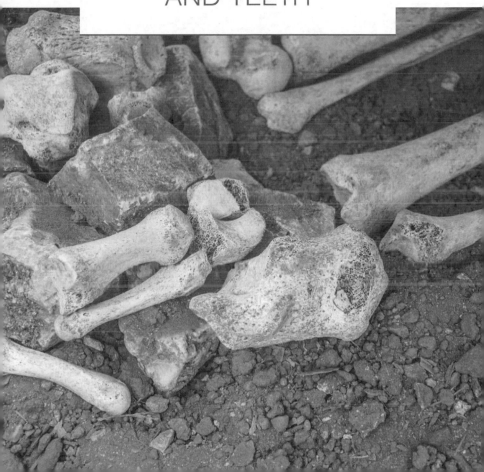

A rchaeologists and paleoanthropologists look to fossils to find clues about human history. Material objects and bones that survive the test of time captivate us. This excitement over objects and bones certainly extends to studying the evolution of human nutrition. Important clues have been provided by fossils—specifically in the form of stones, bones, and teeth—and the general consensus is that our ancestors evolved to consume a generalized diet that includes both plant products and animal material.

Stone Tools

- The invention of stone tools is an aspect of the diet story that has fascinated scientists and the public alike for generations.

- The evolution of tool manufacture and use tells a vibrant story of human evolution. Some of the oldest stone tools have been found in East Africa, and a site called Lomekwi in Kenya has yielded tools that date all the way back to 3.3 million years ago. Some estimates suggest that this predates the evolution of the genus *Homo* by roughly 500,000 years.

- These tools were likely used by Australopithecines, extinct species of East African hominins that were around long before our genus evolved 2.5 million years ago. The discovery of the Lomekwi tools was incredibly surprising because, before this time, the oldest tools on record dated to 2.6 million years ago, from a location in Ethiopia.

- These Ethiopian tools fall into a type of tool kit called Oldowan. The name comes from the Olduvai Gorge in Tanzania, where archaeologist Louis Leakey found the first tools of this type in the 1930s. The Oldowan tool kit includes rounded hammerstones, stone cores that have flake scars around the edges, and stone flakes that were struck from the cores.

- By 1 million years later, around 2.5 to 2.7 million years ago, when our genus *Homo* evolved, tools had changed. Later members of our genus made and used large cutting tools, called Acheulean hand axes. This Acheulean industry is named after the French town where they were first discovered, Saint-Acheul.

- It has been suggested that these early tools were used to butcher game animals, particularly the large hand axes. Increasingly, however, scientists are beginning to think that these tools might have been multipurpose tools that allowed our ancestors not only to butcher animals but also to aid them in the procurement of plant foods.

- The Middle Stone Age, which lasted from about 200,000 to 30,000 years ago, is not only the time when Neanderthals flourished but is also the time when our species, *Homo sapiens sapiens*, evolved.

- During this time, there were many innovations in tool technology. Much more detailed hand axes emerged, as well as more diverse tool kits that emphasized carefully flaked tools.

- By the Late Stone Age in Africa, or the Upper Paleolithic period in Europe, we see incredibly detailed and varied tools being used, ranging from elegantly crafted harpoons to bone needles and awls.

- The earliest stone-tipped spears that we've found date to around 460,000 years ago and were recovered from a site called Kathu Pan in South Africa. If we accept that these spears are the oldest found, which remains controversial, then this pushes the evidence for stone-tipped spears back much further than we expected.

- Other notable spears in the archaeological record include the Schöningen spears, which were found in the late 1990s in a lignite mine in Schöningen, Germany. These wooden spears were found intact in a coal deposit and in association with a large number of bones from large animals.

- Many scientists believe that they might be the first evidence of hunting by the species *Homo heidelbergensis*. The spears date to around 400,000 years, which predates the first appearance of *Homo sapiens* by a few hundred thousand years.

Skeletal Material

- Aspects of an animal's skeleton can tell us a lot about what it eats. Some of the oldest species in the fossil record, called Australopithecines, had some very interesting and distinct cranial features that have allowed anthropologists to infer what their diet might have been.

- A species called *Paranthropus robustus*, for example, lived around 1.5 million years ago in South Africa. Their skulls had large cheekbones that housed large muscles for chewing. In addition, they had a large bony fin on the top of their skull, called a sagittal crest, which anchored the mastication muscles.

- Another species, *Australopithecus afarensis*, lived later, between 3.8 and 2.9 million years ago, and were much smaller in size. They did not have the sagittal crest that would suggest large masticatory muscles. This might tell us that their diet was not composed of the same types of foods that would need powerful masticatory muscles to process.

- Another way that bones have been used to reconstruct ancient diets is a bit more complicated. It is a method called stable isotope analysis, and it has greatly contributed to our understanding of diet composition and habitat. It involves analyzing the distribution of stable isotopes and chemical elements within chemical compounds.

- The Earth and its atmosphere are made up of atoms of different elements, such as carbon, oxygen, and nitrogen, each of which has multiple forms, or isotopes. While the method of isotopic analysis is used across the sciences, anthropologists are largely focused on identifying isotope signatures to help determine what ancient animals were eating.

- The method for skeletal material entails taking a small portion of ancient bone and submitting it to a series of chemical procedures that allows you to extract collagen, a structural protein found throughout our bodies. Once the collagen is extracted, it can be analyzed in a mass spectrometer that measures the amounts of carbon isotopes.

- Animals consuming a diet high in carbon-3 (C3) or carbon-4 (C4) foods will record the diet in their tissues. C3 plants include the majority of the world's herbaceous plants as well as trees and some types of grasses. C4 plants include the majority of grass species as well as sedges. Most of the C4 plants that we are familiar with today are in the form of maize, sugarcane, and sorghum.

- Decades of work on stable isotope analysis among early human ancestors suggests that while some species consumed a diet rich in C3 plants, others consumed a diet rich in C4 foods. Most of the vegetables that we eat today are C3 plants.

- C4 plants are found primarily in temperate grasslands, tropical savannas, or semidesert scrublands, so they do incredibly well in hot, dry places with low levels of carbon dioxide. The Pliocene epoch saw a mass expansion of C4 grasslands, which opened up new dietary niches for early human ancestors—and the animals they consumed.

Dentition

- Teeth, and the information that they convey, are also important. Teeth can tell us about the types of foods consumed, the amount of energy it takes to chew, and patterns of disease—all of which are critical components of an organism's biology.

- Many different types of teeth exist within the animal kingdom. Many reptiles have teeth that all look the same, and many vertebrates shed their teeth and regrow them throughout their lifetime. But mammals, such as humans, are a bit different. We don't replace our teeth multiple times throughout our lives as sharks do. We have jaws that stop growing as adults and shed our teeth only once: in childhood.

- When humans are young, we have deciduous teeth—our baby teeth. These teeth fall out, to be replaced with our adult teeth, which last us (hopefully) a lifetime. We also have teeth that look different from the front of the mouth to the back, called heterodont dentition, which is the pattern we see in most mammals.

- Mammals, including people, have teeth that are designed to do specific jobs, from chewing to shearing. These different types of teeth have shapes that reflect what they are used to do.

  - Incisors (our front teeth) are designed to grasp, scrape, or bring in small pieces of food that will be chewed by other teeth down the line.

○   Next, we have canines, which can be used to puncture.

○   The 2 premolars are positioned directly behind the canines, and along with our molars, the last teeth in our mouths, they make up our posterior dentition (our so-called cheek teeth). The molars and premolars act together to crush, grind, and chew our food before it can be swallowed.

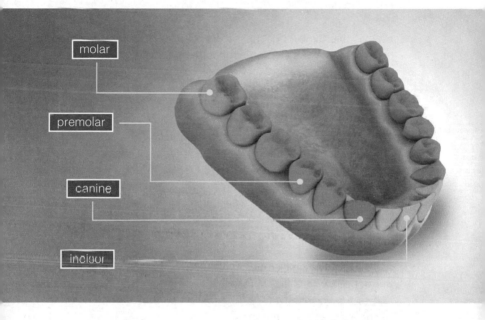

•   We have a veritable tool kit in our mouths that has evolved to mechanically process the foods that we eat, and this tool kit tells the story of an omnivorous diet—one that includes both plant and animal matter.

•   Our teeth are capable of processing a wide array of foods. This matters because teeth are often treated as a bellwether in evolutionary anthropology: If we see drastic changes in dentition throughout human evolution, this likely maps onto changes in diet, which likely map onto changes in reproduction and, in some instances, even social behavior.

- By the time our genus, *Homo*, appeared on the scene more than 2 million years ago, they already had teeth that looked strikingly similar to ours. Their teeth showed generalized dentition that functioned as a tool kit to process and consume both plant and animal matter.

- Before this time, our ancestors had teeth that appeared to be particularly efficient at consuming certain types of food. A chimpanzee, while not our direct relative, is our closest living relative and therefore can tell us a lot about the last common ancestor that we shared before diverging.

- The dentition of a chimpanzee is quite different from ours. While they have the same number and type of teeth as humans, they have much thinner enamel and larger canines. In fact, all of their front teeth are larger, and they also have a gap separating their incisors from their canines, called a diastema. Interestingly, their teeth are positioned in a U shape, called a U-shaped dental arcade, whereas humans have a more parabolic-shaped lower jaw.

- It is impossible to pick an intermediary species, as human evolution did not occur in a linear fashion, but we can pick a species that shows a somewhat ancestral dentition so that we can compare it to chimpanzees and humans.

- *Australopithecus afarensis* is a fossil species that was around a very long time. They had a U-shaped dental arcade, like that of chimpanzees but less extreme, approaching the shape we see in modern humans. They have a diastema, like chimpanzees, but have 2 cusps on their lower third premolars, like humans, though the second cusp is much smaller than ours.

- The human dental arcade is parabolic in shape. We have noticeably smaller incisors and canines, no diastema, and 2 visible cusps on our lower third premolars. While these changes might seem small, they help paint a picture of when our mouths became modern. By the time *Homo erectus* was walking the planet 2 million years ago, they had mouths that looked pretty much just like ours.

- But teeth don't just tell the story of species-specific anatomical traits; they also tell us what an animal was eating. This is certainly true for early members of our genus.

- Some of the best evidence we have of early human diet composition comes from the analysis of dental microwear, the patterns of scratches and pits that form on teeth as a result of their use. The patterning of microwear reflects diet composition, and the foods that an animal consumes leave a "food print" on the teeth.

- Species that shear their food, for example, such as leaf and meat eaters, tend to have a lot of long, parallel scratches on their teeth. Species that are hard-object feeders, such as those that crush nuts and bones, have more pitting, or small circular impressions imbedded in the enamel.

- Dental anthropologists have analyzed the microwear textures of some of our earliest ancestors, such as the early members of the genus *Homo* living around 2 million years ago. The data suggests that they consumed a generalized diet that was dominated by neither hard nor tough foods. So, the microwear data and the dental morphology, or tooth structure, both suggest that our genus was consuming a broad-based, general diet.

- The first project to ever analyze microwear on forager dentition—specifically, from the Hadza population—found that microwear patterns can change quite rapidly, and this can depend on what foods are being consumed. This finding might change the way that some people think about the Pleistocene diet. If we find similar microwear patterns on fossil teeth, it could be an indicator that our ancestors were eating similar types of wild foods.

Suggested Reading

Beeler and Karas, *Throw Your Tooth on the Roof.*

Questions

1. What can stone tools that are found in the archaeological record tell us about diet and hominin behavior?

2. What is dental microwear, and what can it tell us about ancestral diet?

LECTURE
4

DID EATING MEAT
MAKE US HUMAN?

This lecture will trace meat eating through human evolution, starting with evidence of hunting and meat consumption in our closest living relatives, the chimpanzees. You will discover when meat eating hit the scene in human evolution, where data from stone tools and cut marks on bones is key to the story. You will learn about the ways in which animal meat during the Paleolithic period differed from the meat that most people consume today and discover the importance of freshwater and marine foods. You will explore some of the nutritive benefits of consuming animal products as well as data that links meat consumption with disease.

The History of Hunting

- In the 1960s, when renowned anthropologist, primatologist, and ethologist Jane Goodall first observed toolmaking, hunting, and meat eating in wild chimpanzees in Tanzania, many believed their behavior was deviant.

- She made a series of groundbreaking discoveries while studying the chimpanzees of Gombe. In addition to observing them making and creating tools, Jane Goodall also witnessed them hunting and eating monkeys. Up until this point, people erroneously thought that chimpanzees were vegetarians. Many dismissed her observation as an aberration.

- Today, we know that chimpanzees in every ecosystem mainly eat fruit—but also consume the meat of other animals in varying degrees. And in some cases, meat might contribute a significant portion of their calories during certain times of year.

- Chimpanzees are critically relevant to the discussion of when human ancestors began hunting because, while we did not evolve from chimpanzees, we share a common ancestor, and chimpanzees are the species to which we are most closely related.

- So, studying how chimpanzees acquire meat tells us something about the potential capabilities of our earliest ancestors. If chimpanzees do it—and quite successfully—then that gives us an insight into what our earliest ancestors might also have been capable of.

- Chimpanzees tend to hunt in groups, and they largely target smaller primate species. Some estimates suggest that they eat about 35 different vertebrate species. While solo hunts do occur, the majority of hunting is social.

- Cooperation in hunting has long been theorized by behavioral scientists as a means to increase success rates. Chimpanzee researchers have also posited that there's a strong positive relationship between the number of chimpanzees on a hunt and the odds that it will be successful.

- At Taï National Park in Côte d'Ivoire, West Africa, primatologist Christophe Boeuoh has witnessed meat-sharing behavior after a kill in which those who participated in the hunt are rewarded with meat.

- Other intriguing data has come from Senegal and the field site of primatologist Jill Pruetz. who reported the first data on chimpanzees making and using spears for hunting. Interestingly, it turns out that female chimpanzees are more likely to use tools for hunting.

- Many researchers believe that if chimpanzees can hunt—and do so in varying environments—then certainly early human ancestors hunted and consumed meat in a fashion similar to wild chimpanzees.

Targeting Animals for Consumption

- The diet of our early ancestors was probably something like the diet of chimpanzees: omnivorous, with large amounts of fruit, leaves, bark, flowers, insects, and meat. While individual communities of chimpanzees can eat a lot of meat, meat is only estimated to make up about 3% of the diet.

- The most robust evidence that we have for meat eating in early members of our genus comes from butchery marks found on animal bones. The actions used to access bone marrow or to skin an animal leave distinct impressions: cut and percussion marks.

- Some of the earliest purported evidence of cut marks are controversial. They date to around 3.4 million years ago and were found at a site called Dikika in Ethiopia. One of the reasons that these interpretations remain so controversial is likely due to the fact that these fossils date to the time of Australopithecines, ancient ancestors who don't share our genus.

- While tantalizing, many researchers suggest that future finds that date to this time period are needed to confirm hunting this early. There is, however, well-accepted evidence of cut marks from Gona, Ethiopia, around 2.6 million years ago—around the time that our genus, *Homo*, evolved. A fossilized ankle bone of an extinct zebra species was found to have markings on it that indicated that it was butchered.

- In Kenya, at a site called Kanjera, excavated by archaeologist Thomas Plummer, one of the largest assemblages of stone tools and animal bones with butchery marks was found. The Kanjera collection is impressive, with 3700 animal fossils and 2900 stone tools dating to around 2 million years ago.

- The tools associated with these finds don't necessarily seem like they would be linked with routine big-game hunting. Many of these tools look like they were used for cutting or pounding, and this tool industry, called Oldowan, did not include spears or stone tips to haft to spears. Arrowheads were not even in existence.

- So, how did our ancestors hunt the animals that they were eating? The hunting-versus-scavenging debate that ensues is heated. Some anthropologists are stalwart in their belief that early humans, and our ancestors, were accomplished hunters. Others are equally adamant that it is likely that the earliest members of our genus were scavengers.

- Beyond hunting and scavenging, there are many people who believe that rather than being hunters, our early ancestors were the hunted. And there is fossil evidence that some people believe might support this perspective.

Differences in Types of Meat

- When we're thinking about hunting during the Paleolithic period, we're not talking about the same types of game animals that we would think about today. The type of meat that early humans ate was quite different from the type of meat that we eat now. Compared to the meat that you get from your local market or butcher, wild-game meat is low in saturated fats and relatively high in polyunsaturated fatty acids.

- Early hunters living in the Paleolithic (also called the Pleistocene) period did not eat only muscle tissue. Much like contemporary foragers today, our ancestors likely consumed all edible portions of the carcass, including organs, bone marrow, and sometimes even the gastrointestinal tract of the animal.

- For many decades, big-game meat received almost exclusive attention as the most important (and only) animal protein in human evolution. But this bias may not be accurate. Contemporary interpretations of the evolutionary diet are changing—specifically in the ways in which we think about animal contributions to the diet.

- For example, the Hadza foragers of Tanzania eat many different types of game meat. While small-game meat is critical to the forager diet, the image of a diminutive dik-dik (a small antelope) poses a striking contrast to much of the imagery of our Paleolithic past. And while we know that our ancestors targeted and consumed megafauna, such as mammoths, the small animals might have also made a big contribution.

- This extends to other types of meat, such as fish and other types of coastal resources. Increasingly, both marine and freshwater foods are moving to the forefront of dietary models of human evolution. This is based on new data that suggests that our ancestors exploited coastal habitats and may have even followed the coastlines during migration routes out of Africa.

- Some anthropologists argue that the exploitation of marine resources, such as fish, shellfish, and tortoises, was critical to our evolutionary success. The timeline is debated, however.

- Other than foraging populations, humans no longer target the same types of large mammals that they did in the Pliocene epoch. This is not the case for fish. Marine resources represent the last wild animals that we hunt in large numbers—all over the world. Research suggests, however, that we will likely be the last generation to do so.

- There are good reasons why marine resources are targeted today, as well as in our evolutionary past. They are key foods for nutritionists and researchers who reconstruct diet. Docosahexaenoic acid is an omega-3 fatty acid that is a primary structural component of the human brain and cerebral cortex.

- Foods that are high in polyunsaturated fats—specifically omega-3 fatty acids—are important for maintaining good health. In particular, docosahexaenoic acid has been shown to play a role in brain, eye, and heart health.

Meat Consumption: Health and Disease

- In addition to being a high-quality food item that may have contributed to neural expansion in our ancestors, animal protein has other nutritional benefits—for example, in preventing iron deficiency, or anemia. Around the world, iron is one of the most commonly deficient nutrients. This might be linked to the fact that it has low bioavailability, which refers to the ease and speed at which a nutrient makes its way from the food to the target tissue.

- There are 2 types of dietary iron: heme and nonheme iron. Nonheme iron is found in both plant foods and animal tissues. This type of iron is poorly absorbed and has low bioavailability. Heme iron, on the other hand, comes from hemoglobin and myoglobin found in animals. This type of iron is very bioavailable. Heme iron is also known to increase the absorption of nonheme iron, which means that meat is the best source of iron that we can consume.

- While meat allowed our ancestors to outcompete other species— it is full of micronutrients and essential fatty acids and in almost all cases is a fantastic energy source—the association of red meat with chronic diseases is a swiftly expanding and highly controversial area of research, yet more data is being collected that supports this association.

- Coronary artery disease, stroke, hypertension, and other cardiac and vascular diseases, as well as some cancers and type 2 diabetes, have all been linked, in varying degrees, with the consumption of red meat. Incidentally, they're also among the leading causes of death worldwide.

- The consumption of Neu5Gc, short for *N*-glycolylneuraminic acid, which we get from eating red meat, has been correlated with cancer. While more data is needed, this adds to the growing epidemiological literature that suggests a link between eating red meat and increased risks of carcinomas, atherosclerosis, and type 2 diabetes.

Suggested Reading

Gibbons, "The Evolution of Diet."

Gremillion, *Ancestral Appetites*.

Marean, "When the Sea Saved Humanity."

Stanford, "Chimpanzee Hunting Behavior and Human Evolution."

Questions

1. Why is evidence of tool use among wild chimpanzees an important discovery for human evolution?

2. While the image of "man the hunter" is one that dominates public perception of our ancestral past, how accurate is that depiction?

INSECTS: THE OTHER WHITE MEAT

All around the world, people eat bugs. From beetles, to scorpions, to stink bugs, our winged and legged friends, while small in size, can make big contributions to our diet. They are highly nutritious—often packed with fat, protein, and lots of vitamins and minerals—and are much more sustainable than other types of meat. While the practice of eating insects is not mainstream yet, many Americans are starting to see the appeal.

Entomophagy

- The practice of eating bugs is called entomophagy, and it has been around for most of human history, if not all of it. Even though the practice dates to antiquity, the appreciation of insects as food has not gained popular momentum in the United States until recently.

- A recent article in *TIME* outlined 20 bug recipes from famous United States chefs around the country and noted how bugs are making a wave in the foodie movement. With all of the different flavors and textures, and the versatility with which you can prepare them, master chefs are singing the praises of cooking with bugs.

- David George Gordon, the so-called bug chef and author of *The Eat-a-Bug Cookbook*, contributed a recipe for deep-fried tarantulas. He freezes them, removes the abdomen, burns off the hair with a butane torch, and then deep-fries them in tempura. He claims that they are always a big hit with diners.

- Another chef from Louisiana has even suggested that it's possible to use a net in your own backyard. He encourages people to swing a net around during hot summer nights to catch dragonflies. Once caught, you can freeze them and then prepare them just as you would fried soft-shell crab.

Honey

- This use of bugs as foodstuff is not new. All around the world, throughout history, people have turned to insects for nutrition. The one that we are most likely familiar with—and don't think twice about eating—is honey.

- Honey is actually regurgitated nectar, or bee vomit, from worker bees. Honey is one of the most energy-dense foods in nature. It's a concentrated source of glucose and fructose and contains trace amounts of several essential vitamins and minerals. It also has components that act as preservatives.

- And this is just liquid honey. As soon as you add bee larvae, it also becomes a good source of protein, fat, and B vitamins.

- Many researchers are now looking to honey as a key food in human evolution. It has received much less attention than meat or plant products, but it's highly likely that honey—and the products of bee hives, such as larvae and pollen—were important foods for our ancestors.

- When we are aiming to look deep into evolutionary time, studying the diet of apes can help us piece together the puzzle of the evolution of human nutrition.

- When we see something that all great apes eat, in every ecosystem, that's also consumed by human populations around the world, we can deduce that this might have been a key food to our species' evolution. This extends to fruit, plant foods, insects, and the products of insects, such as honey.

- Gorillas and orangutans, for example, have been shown to consume honey. Wild chimpanzees, great apes from Africa, have been shown to eat honey in every habitat where we can study.

- In addition, people all around the world highly value honey as a food. Across Latin America, Africa, Asia, and Australia, many populations—both contemporary and historical—consider or have considered honey to be one of the most important foods in their diet.

- Among the Hadza, honey is highly valued. It's considered to be the most highly ranked food, placed well above meat. Men and teenage boys are the honey hunters among the Hadza, although everyone enjoys the spoils of their foraging trips.

Honey as Part of the Human Diet

- Honey is also intriguing beyond these ethnographic and cross-cultural examples. It appears that honey has been a part of the human diet for a very long time, possibly for millions of years.

- Our ancestors could have easily targeted hives with the stone tools that they had available, and honey, with the added boost of protein and larvae, would have been an ideal food for an enlarging brain.

- Brains are very metabolically expensive, so during our evolutionary past, our ancestors would have had to rely on some type, or types, of energy-rich foods to fuel that neural expansion.

- Honey is easy to consume and digest, and it's very energetically dense. Despite these traits, it hasn't received as much attention as other candidate foods in evolutionary reconstructions of diet.

- The ability to find and exploit beehives with stone tools would have been an incredible innovation that allowed our early ancestors to nutritionally outcompete other species. So, honey was likely at least a part of the energy source that helped fuel our enlarging brains.

- Other lines of evidence also suggest that honey has long been a part of the human sweet tooth. We have data from actual teeth that tell the story of a long connection with the sweet stuff.

- One of the only cases of prehistoric dentistry on record is evidence of beeswax being used as a Neolithic dental filling—on a 6500-year-old tooth from Slovenia. The canine in question was found with a crown made out of beeswax.

- Another line of evidence for the long use of honey comes from beeswax residues found in ancient Neolithic pottery that dates to around 9000 years ago.

- The chemical properties of beeswax, mainly the fats that it contains, make it resistant to degradation. This allows archaeologists to identify containers where honey may have been housed. This has intriguing implications for the transition from foraging to agriculture.

- We also find fascinating evidence in many examples of rock art around the world. Upper Paleolithic sites, dating from about 50,000 to 10,000 years ago, include several depictions of honey and bees. These artistic renderings can be found on caves and rock faces in Europe, India, Australia, and Southern Africa. Some of the most abundant rock art showing different honey-related activities is found in Spain.

- Other forms of ancient art and material culture also show how important honey collection and consumption were. The earliest written record of bees in China is recorded on inscriptions on animal bones dating to 3000 years ago. And a famed jar of honey was found in King Tut's tomb in Egypt, also dating to around 3000 years ago.

Beekeeping

- Some historians of apiculture, or the keeping of bees, contend that the earliest form of beekeeping was nest ownership. Once people began settling down in the Neolithic period, they would mark hives to indicate that the hive, and its contents, were their property.

- At some point, possibly around the 18th century, people began to attempt to domesticate wild bees in artificial hives. The 19th century saw an explosion of beekeeping technology all around the world, where hive construction, selective breeding, and honey collection were perfected.

- Hives that can't be transported, or where comb can't be moved or manipulated without damaging it, are called fixed-comb hives. These aren't used very widely anymore but are still popular in

some areas around the world, particularly in the developing world, where beekeeping is part of the local economy and livelihood is dependent on it.

- Today, most beekeeping is done with movable-frame hives or top-bar hives. Commercial beekeeping is a very lucrative business, with recent estimates suggesting that the honey business yields about $317 million in profits on an annual basis.

- Interestingly, the "ick" factor seems to be almost nonexistent when it comes to eating honey. This extends to eating bee pollen, or even propolis, which is a sticky residue that bees collect from buds that is used to seal small gaps in a beehive. One reason for this might be because we are aware of the nutritional properties of honey.

- We're so used to having honey as part of our cuisine, we don't even think about the fact that it's created by insects. Honey is nectar that has been extracted from flowers and then stored in the stomach of an insect—but we don't often think about that when we go to sweeten our tea with it.

- Often when something seems "normal" to us, or is just a "normal" part of our diet, it's because we're socialized to feel that way. We're comfortable eating certain cuisines because we have been raised to do so. People viewing our culture might have some very strong reactions to some of the things that we routinely consume. This negative reaction to insect consumption is something that insect-eating enthusiasts are trying to combat.

Sustainability

- Bees and their habitats are threatened, so quite often, discussions about wild foods come back to the crux of the issue: sustainability. The harsh reality is that bees are disappearing around the world. Scientists call it colony collapse disorder, and it's when there is a dead colony, which means no adult bees, or only dead bees, and a living queen.

- No single cause has been agreed upon, but the Environmental Protection Agency and the U.S. Department of Agriculture list several factors that may contribute to the problem. These include:

  - invasive species of mites that are pests to beehives,

  - new or emerging diseases and parasites that negatively impact bee populations,

  - possible pesticide poisoning,

  - stress due to transportation between multiple locations, or

  - habitat modification or loss.

- The loss of these tiny workers can cause a lot of damage to our ecosystem—and to our dinner table. Bees work really hard to bring all kinds of foods to our table, not just honey. We have bees to thank for many of our favorite foods, including almonds, apples, and blueberries.

- There's a lot of work being done, in terms of grassroots movements and community organization as well as policy changes and work done by the U.S. Department of Agriculture. Many scientists, environmentalists, farmers, and apiarists are working together to combat the situation.

- Environmental and political links also exist between our dinner plates and other insect populations in a slightly different capacity.

- Many believe that entomophagy is the wave of the future. Supporters argue that it's a highly sustainable, ethical, and safe way to reduce pest insects without the use of pesticides.

- Proponents of the "insects as food" movement argue that raising and harvesting insects require less land than raising pigs, cows, or sheep and that insects need much less food than these larger animals.

- Other purported benefits of a diet rich in insects includes fewer emitted greenhouse gases and a food that is easier to farm. Proponents argue that because bugs have a shorter life cycle, they can easily be raised in urban and peri-urban environments, freeing up forested areas.

- The United Nations agrees that insects do, indeed, have a much smaller carbon footprint. This suggests that insects might be able to provide a sustainable source of nutrition for an ever-growing global population.

- Besides the psychological barrier that many people in the West have in regard to eating insects, there are other hurdles that have to be cleared before we can start incorporating insects into the mainstream diet.

- There's a lack of federal regulation on edible insects, so we still need quite a bit of research on environmental impact, feasibility, and sustainability before it becomes common to order insects at your favorite restaurant. We also need more information on exactly how food-grade insect farms can develop and thrive.

- Food fairs and exotic food markets are starting to turn the tide. Some popular companies make all of their snacks using cricket flour for protein, and other insect-based proteins are popping up in natural food markets throughout the United States.

- You can also purchase edible insects from retailers who specialize in selling insects for consumption. But for people who know their insects and how to harvest them, they can certainly obtain bugs from local areas, such as local parks, woodlands, and along streams and rivers.

Suggested Reading

Crane, *The World History of Beekeeping and Honey Hunting*.
Crittenden, "The Importance of Honey Consumption in Human Evolution."
Oaklander, "20 Delicious Bug Recipes from Chefs."

Questions

1. Why has the United Nations recently endorsed edible insects as one of the foods of the future?

2. What does the evidence of honey hunting from around the world tell us about the relationship between humans and honeybees?

LECTURE
6

WAS THE STONE AGE MENU MOSTLY VEGETARIAN?

The likely diet of our ancestors was a broad-based one that included both plant and animal material. The introduction of meat to the early human diet most certainly altered the course of human evolution, but plant foods also played a significant role in our ancestral diet. In this lecture, you will explore this critical role, examining data from teeth and plant microfossils that are drastically changing what we thought we knew about the diet of our ancestors. You will also learn about underground storage organs, commonly referred to as tubers, and the models of evolutionary anthropology for which they play an essential part.

Evidence of Our Reliance on Plants

- Generally, primates are omnivores. This means that they take advantage of a wide range of foods, including leaves, fruits, flowers, nuts, seeds, and small animals. There is a surprising amount of diversity of diet composition that we see among living primates.

- We know, based on stable isotope studies, that early members of our genus began to show an increased reliance on plants that utilized a carbon-4 (or C4) pathway. These foods would likely have been from a grassland habitat. This differs from a tropical forest ecosystem that likely housed the foods of our much older, and more apelike, ancestors.

- Now we know that our genus enjoyed a long incubation time, in evolutionary terms, in arid high-temperature ecosystems. This means that we can safely say that our early ancestors consumed C4 plants that would have provided a substantial portion of their diet. What these specific foods were remains somewhat elusive.

- Up until recently, our ability to extract information on plant eating from the archaeological record was limited. We had a few tantalizing clues, such as plant motifs in Indian, Australian, Indonesian, Sri Lankan, and even North American rock art. Despite the visible clues they offer, they date to recent times in human evolutionary history.

- Although not a wealth of data, there is also some intriguing evidence on the use of woven plant fibers in human evolution. This was an ingenious Paleolithic technology that was possibly used in many ways, such as using plant fibers as fishing net weights or to string necklaces.

- But how do we find evidence of plant eating from earlier time periods—definitive evidence that plants play a role in deep evolutionary time? Here's where the study of plant fossils, or archaeobotany, comes into the picture.

- Plant fossils are known as phytoliths. They are microscopic pieces of silica that form in plant cells when soluble silica in the ground is absorbed by the roots and then taken up by a plant.

- Silica is commonly composed of sand or quartz, and because pieces of silica are somewhat like pieces of hard glass, they're preserved in the archaeological record—long after the plants that housed them have died and decayed.

- Phytolith analysis, as well as pollen and starch granule analysis, can tell us a lot about prehistoric diet composition.

- While we don't often think of plants when we think of fossils, it turns out that phytoliths teach us quite a bit about the types of plants and trees that were used by humans—and our ancestors. We can learn what types of plants were used in crafting material objects and in fire burning, although this is fairly recent in human evolution.

- Plant macrofossil data can tell us something about diet. Evidence from Europe suggests that ancient humans during the Middle Paleolithic period (from around 200,000 to about 45,000 years ago) ate wild pistachios, acorns, almonds, and legumes.

- Starch grains have also been found on ancient grinding stones dating to the Middle and Upper Paleolithic period, which is critically important to the discussion of the role plant foods played in the ancient human diet. They've been found all around the world by archaeologists, in sites in Asia, Israel, and Europe.

- When archaeologists find grinding stone implements with starch grains on their surface, this provides key information about the ability of ancestral humans to process plants in a very complex way, well before the advent of agriculture.

- Making flour meant that ancestral humans may have also had the ability to store flour, which has implications for the transport of resources—something that is very interesting to archaeologists.

- Using associated data from the archaeology sites, such as the presence of domesticated grains, scientists believe that the first reported flour production in Europe dates to almost 30,000 years ago. This is about 20,000 years before domesticated plants came on the scene. This indicates that flour was being produced first from wild plants before shifting to flour from domesticated sources.

- Starch grains, grass, ferns, and other miscellaneous plants have also been recovered on grinding stones from Australia dating to around 27,000 years ago.

- When phytoliths or starch granules are found in teeth, this gives us direct evidence that an animal was consuming a particular type of plant. Recent strides in extracting phytoliths from dental calculus have yielded some fascinating clues about what our ancestors were eating.

- Anthropologist and phytolith expert Dr. Amanda Henry discovered both phytoliths and starch grains in the hardened dental calculus of Neanderthal fossils from Iraq and Belgium.

- These data show that Neanderthals—often hailed for their meat consumption—consumed a wide range of plants. They recovered microfossils of grasses, seeds, dates, legumes, and even wild barley. Even more fascinating, some of these starches show damage that clearly indicates that the plants they were consuming were cooked.

- Other techniques of recovering information at this level include analyzing actual food residues found on ancient pottery and stone tools.

- Another line of evidence that we can use from fossil teeth is that of microwear. The foods that an animal eats leave distinct "food prints" on the teeth in the form of pits, grooves, and scratches. These markings can tell us the types of food that were being consumed. They tell us the general traits of a food, such as if it was hard or soft.

- The dental microwear data suggests that our earliest ancestors relied on plant foods to varying degrees. Some targeted hard foods while others were more generalized.

- Beyond the fossil evidence, we can also use data from contemporary foragers to inform our interpretations about the significance of plant foods in dietary reconstructions.

- Plant foods are an important component of the diet for all foragers on the planet. This even extends to arctic foragers, whose diet contains fewer plant foods but still relies on plant contributions for some months out of the year.

The Importance of Tubers

- A few plant foods that are really important to the Hadza foragers are baobab fruit and marula nuts, but the most significant plant food in their diet is tubers, a key food in the evolution of human nutrition. Tubers, which can be thought of as underground storage organs, are a type of plant found in almost every diet of modern human foragers.

- They're not only popular with foraging populations but also in the diet of populations from the postindustrialized West. Americans eat many tubers, such as potatoes, sweet potatoes, yams, and summer squash.

- The degree to which people rely on these foods varies around the world, both regionally and seasonally, and many scientists believe that our species has had a long and fruitful relationship with these fibrous plants.

- Tubers are present in the cross-cultural record as a major dietary staple, or even as what some refer to as a fallback food, meaning that people can fall back on tubers when nothing else is around.

- While Hadza tubers might be low in fat and protein, they are relatively high in fiber and simple carbohydrates and might also be an important source of water, particularly during the dry season.

- Other types of tubers around the world have different characteristics. Some are more nutritious than Hadza tubers while others are less so. Some have much less fiber, and some have toxins that make them inedible unless roasted. This becomes a critical part of the story that links tubers and fire.

- The sole fact that tubers are routinely targeted by foraging groups all around the world makes them a good candidate for a Paleolithic food.

- The wear markings on 2-million-year-old stone tools from Kenya match the wear markings from Hadza tuber processing on replica tools. This suggests that by at least 2 million years ago, our ancestors were very likely exploiting tubers and other underground storage organs.

- Tubers don't only help tell the story of the evolution of the human diet; they may also tell us something about human life history and the nature of cooperation.

- At some point in our evolutionary history, females of the species began giving birth to large-brained and very helpless infants. These babies needed high levels of investment that extended way beyond infancy. How did a Paleolithic mother take care of herself, which included increased caloric demands during pregnancy and lactation, as well as take care of multiple dependent young?

- This has been a hot topic among biologists and anthropologists for decades, and it continues to be something that researchers ponder. Despite several different hypotheses, there appears to be one answer seems to make the most sense: Pleistocene mothers relied on help.

- Ethologist and anthropologist Dr. Sarah Blaffer Hrdy has devoted the majority of her career to exploring this topic throughout our evolutionary history. She argues that one of the hallmarks of our species is our extraordinary ability to engage in cooperative child-rearing.

- She maintains that help during the Paleolithic period likely came from many sources—fathers, siblings, grandparents, extended family, and friends. This assistance would have taken the shape of actual food sharing as well as behavioral investment.

- Another model highlighting the significance of cooperative-care networks has received equal attention to Dr. Hrdy's cooperative breeding model. It is called the grandmother hypothesis, and it argues for the special—and critical—role that grandmothers played in human evolution.

- The hypothesis is based largely on fieldwork that was collected in the 1980s and 1990s by anthropologist Dr. Kristen Hawkes and colleagues James O'Connell and Nicholas Blurton Jones.

- The trio of researchers spent a lot of time in East Africa working among the Hadza. As they were collecting data on food provisioning and foraging behavior across men and women, they noticed that post-menopausal women—grandmothers—were top producers.

- This extended to tuber collection. These grandmothers would often return home at the end of a daily foraging excursion with upward of 8 or 9 kilograms of tubers—more than enough to feed themselves and still have ample leftovers.

- Armed with these intriguing data, the researchers proposed a revolutionary hypothesis: that during human evolution, grandmothers were able to increase their own lifetime reproductive success by ceasing ovulation. Even though they were ending their own reproduction, they were still investing quite heavily in the growth and development of their grandchildren.

- So, women were able to increase their own lifetime reproductive success by changing gears later in life, switching from investing in their children to investing in the children of their children. This grandmother hypothesis has now become one of the most influential hypotheses in human evolution and biology, and it was largely based on the importance of tubers as a critical food.

- It's important to note that tubers are exclusively collected by women for every population in which we have good ecological data. These sex differences, in terms of resources targeted and consumed, also have real implications for reproduction.

- For decades, anthropologists have been asking detailed questions about why we see such a distinct sexual division of labor between the sexes. In the overwhelming majority of foraging populations, men target animal matter while women tend to focus on plant foods.

- We see sex differences not only in the types of foods targeted by foragers but also in diet composition. While the majority of the data remains anecdotal, the picture we get is one in which men consume greater quantities of meat while women consume greater quantities of plant foods.

- Tubers have not only been linked to reproduction but have also consistently entered into the debate on brain evolution. Some scientists believe that tubers are low-quality foods and are likely too energy-poor to nourish and sustain large-brained, large-bodied creatures like our early ancestors.

- Others, alternatively, have long touted that tubers are a smoking-gun food in human evolution, providing much-needed glucose to the expanding brains of our ancestors. Data on other types of plants, such as sedges, might have been adequate to fuel neural expansion.

Suggested Reading

Gibbons, "The Evolution of Diet."
Gremillion, *Ancestral Appetites*.
Hrdy, *Mothers and Others*.

Questions

1. What is a phytolith, and what information can it provide to scientists interested in reconstructing historic diet?

2. Based on the evidence, was the Stone Age menu mostly meat based or mostly vegetarian?

COOKING AND THE CONTROL OF FIRE

The control of fire stands out as the most important milestone in our evolutionary history. Many believe that fire was critical to the origin of our species. It likely provided much-needed warmth, light, and protection from predators. Other touted benefits included increased social cohesion from campfire storytelling and the use of fire for food preparation. Roasting, boiling, and baking are food-processing techniques that are invariably human, but when did our ancestors start practicing them? And how?

The Taming of Fire

- French gastronomist Jean-Anthelme Brillat-Savarin is credited with being one of the first people to claim that the taming of fire is what allowed us to become the dominant species that we are today. In 1825, he linked the controlled use of fire for cooking with increased meat eating in human evolution.

- His thoughts on cooking were largely ignored, being overshadowed by his much more widespread thoughts on food, appetite, cuisine, and gastronomy in general. His ideas weren't really picked up again until the late 1990s, when anthropologist Richard Wrangham and his colleagues proposed a radical hypothesis: that cooking is the "hinge on which human evolution turned."

- This team has argued that In our evolutionary past, the advent of cooking was responsible for our sociality, intelligence, and even the way that we choose our mates.

- This hypothesis, aptly named the cooking hypothesis, while wildly popular, remains quite controversial among anthropologists and archaeologists who study fire. This might be because evidence of the first control of fire is very difficult to come by archaeologically.

- Some of the oldest evidence for the controlled use of fire dates to around 1 million years ago in South Africa, in a place called Wonderwerk Cave. The archaeologists who work at this site have found burned bone and ash from cooking plants. They claim that these are clear indications of fire being deliberately burned inside the cave.

- There's also contested evidence found in Israel dating to around 790,000 years ago. Archaeologists at this site report the presence of what they say is deliberately burned seeds, wood, and flint. They argue that not only do they have evidence of specific locations being used, such as hearths, but that 3 of the 6 species of burned plant material recovered are edible. This includes wild barley, olive, and grape.

- Scientists that dispute the evidence from these old sites claim that dating techniques and methodology aren't able to distinguish between natural brush fires and controlled fires created by humans, or our ancestors.

- For researchers who don't believe in the antiquity of fire, some of the oldest agreed-upon dates are found from hearths dating to around 250,000 years ago in Israel, where ash deposits in a cave were found to be close to 1.5 inches thick.

- More recent evidence dates to the time of the Neanderthals, from around 200,000 years to 30,000 years ago, and it's some of the most exciting and interesting data on the controlled use of fire. Neanderthals are credited with being early masters of pyrotechnological knowledge. At a site in France, archaeologists have found evidence that lignite, a combustible sedimentary rock, was routinely imported to the area as fuel from as far as 6 miles away.

- Other sites in Europe have yielded what researchers believe are stone-lined hearths. Neanderthals have also been credited with boiling. Dental calculus from fossil Neanderthal teeth produced unmistakable evidence for the consumption of cooked plant foods.

- We're not sure how early humans and their ancestors were utilizing fire to cook food. Most believe that they were simply laying food on top of the fire, or very near to the coals—what we would call roasting.

- Others believe that they were also boiling their food, using a few different techniques. Stones that have been heated can be transferred into containers made out of hides, gut, or even ostrich eggshells to heat the water to a boil. Once the water in the container is hot enough, it can be used to cook whatever is inside the container.

- While the containers rarely survive the archaeological record, the boiling stones do, allowing archaeologists to recover them from sites and study their properties. It's thought that hot stones were also likely used for pit baking in holes in the ground that acted like an oven.

- Some scientists even believe that you don't need hot stones to boil water and that, depending on the container, one could boil water in perishable containers directly over a small flame.

- Either technique works, and we have archaeological evidence from the upper Paleolithic period, from around 50,000 to 10,000 years ago, that supports boiling.

- Some of the oldest pottery, dating to around 20,000 years ago, has been found in a cave in China. The fragments show scorch marks, indicating that the pottery was used in cooking. Ancient pottery dating to this time has also been found on the Japanese islands and in Siberia.

- Interestingly, potsherds can also be analyzed for residue content to help archaeologists figure out what people may have been cooking in those pots. Lipids recovered from Japanese pots suggest that the people making and using these containers were consuming freshwater marine food resources. Other potsherds from China show that the containers were being used to cook plant material.

The Benefits of Heating Our Food

- The idea behind the raw food movement is that all animals in the animal kingdom easily live off of raw food, so why should humans not do so?

- We know that many foods—particularly plant foods, nuts and seeds, oils, and even honey—are entirely edible raw. The problem is that it's very difficult, if not impossible, to get all of the energy that we need from an entirely raw diet.

- Many proponents of this type of diet report better physical and emotional well-being. But several clinical studies on raw foodists have reached the conclusion that there are negative energy consequences of eating a totally raw diet. Some results even suggest that reduced reproductive function can be a consequence of foregoing cooked foods.

- With regard to whether our bodies evolved to eat a diet that is primarily raw, the evidence appears to support the idea of cooked foods being integral to our evolving species. It does make sense to think about a portion of the early human diet being raw, just like today. But at some point in our evolutionary history, cooked foods entered into the world of food processing.

- Cooking is only one type of traditional food processing, but it's the one that tends to get the most attention. Other methods of traditional food processing include pounding, winnowing, cutting, fermenting, and peeling. All of these actions can significantly augment nutritional accessibility for human digestion. This is also true with cooking.

- There must be benefits to cooking if our ancestors began doing it regularly and every known human society cooks their food. Cooking breaks down some indigestible plant parts, such as fibers, for easier fermentation and digestion. It also aids in the deactivation of some toxins that may be barriers to digestion. Cooking also makes it easier to chew certain types of food, such as meat.

- Scientists such as Richard Wrangham have spent a lot of time pulling together data on chewing. He and his colleagues have estimated that our ancestors, if they were eating a diet similar to great apes, would have spent about 42% of the day chewing their raw food.

- Comparable data on chewing time among people who live in small-scale foraging societies eating wild foods that contain high amounts of fiber spend about 1/5th to 1/10th as much time chewing their food. This equates to less than 12% of time in a 14-hour day. These differences in chewing time have been linked to the ease with which we can consume cooked food.

- We have mouths and teeth that can more easily break up cooked food—smaller teeth, less powerful jaws, and smaller guts than our ancestors.

- Many scientists support the idea that cooking is a large part of the story of our evolved diet. Other scientists think that while it is plausible, we simply don't have good evidence of controlled fire that goes back long enough.

- Those that don't buy such an old date for fire also point to the anatomical differences that we see in the fossil record. They argue that what some link with the beginning of cooking might be, in fact, linked with other processing techniques or simply with a shift to high-quality foods that weren't heated.

- A few of these candidate foods include honey and some species of tubers, particularly the really fibrous species, such as the ones that the Hadza eat. Tubers are also part of the story with cooking. They have been an integral part of the cooking hypothesis from its inception, suggesting that their digestibility increases with roasting.

- Research conducted on the Hadza population by Alyssa Crittenden and Stephanie Schnorr showed that while cooking for long stretches of time certainly breaks down the starch, making it more digestible, brief roasting periods seem to have negligible effects. Brief roasting might have other benefits.

- Professor Nate Dominy and his colleagues found that roasting helps to mechanically break down tubers. Fire helps decrease some of the toughness of the internal tissues of the tubers, effectively making them easier to chew. And eating food that is easier to chew means that you can eat more of it. So, by lessening the costs of mastication, or chewing, you're also effectively lessening the costs of digestion.

- Further research determined that roasting, an activity undertaken by the Hadza, may have other benefits, including making the tubers easier to peel, which would make them easier to eat— meaning that you could eat more of them faster.

- Some scientists argue that early humans would have been able to consume small amounts of raw meat, much like contemporary raw foodists, maybe by pounding it or processing it in a way that allowed the meat to be more easily chewed. Other suggestions are that it might have been dried, sort of like beef jerky.

- We can eat raw meat in small amounts, or processed very finely. Something like steak tartare is a delicacy and is basically spiced raw beef that's finely chopped or minced. But steak tartare is not the same thing as wild-game meat, and many scientists believe that it would be almost impossible to eat a large amount of meat raw. We simply don't have the mandibular jaw power to make that happen.

- We've evolved to eat our meat cooked. We know that cooked meat is easier to digest and that cooking eradicates bacteria. We also know that our ancestors were likely roasting or boiling their meat. But we still don't really know, definitively, when our ancestors began eating cooked meat routinely.

- It all depends on what dates you prefer for the evidence of fire. It's also important to remember that many scientists now believe that the foods in our evolutionary past that paved the way for our species might have been largely plant based. There's a general consensus in the scientific and nutritional communities that both meat and plant foods were critical in our ancestral diet.

Suggested Reading

Wrangham, *Catching Fire*.

Questions

1. Why is the evidence of the first control of fire controversial?

2. What are the benefits of cooking food, particularly meat?

THE NEOLITHIC REVOLUTION

During the so-called Neolithic Revolution, we transitioned from being hunters and gatherers eating a mostly wild diet to being agriculturalists eating a diet of domesticated foods. In this lecture, you will discover what would prompt large populations of people to drastically change their subsistence strategy, and you will learn which plants and animals were first domesticated and where.

Plant Domestication

- There are several hypotheses as to why humans decided to take up agriculture, and many of them differ depending on where in the world is being discussed.

- One of the most-often-cited hypotheses has to do with climate change. During the Late Pleistocene, there were massive climatic fluctuations, and then when we hit the Holocene, temperatures evened out. This climate shift is thought to have been the main trigger for such a massive shift in subsistence behavior.

- The first person to propose a climatic impetus for the beginning of domestication was Raphael Pumpelly, an American geologist, in 1908. This oasis theory was associated with the idea that when climates dried out, people and animals would converge on so-called oases to survive.

- Although originally proposed by Pumpelly, this idea wasn't popularized until 1928, when it was reintroduced by V. Gordon Childe, a very well-known archaeologist of his time.

- Since its initial iteration, some variant of climatic determinism has colored the way that most people think about the origins of agriculture, particularly in the Near East during the Late

Pleistocene and Early Holocene. Many of the top scholars in archaeology argue that climate change persisted as the key initial force in the development of cultivation.

- Since 1928, however, our understanding of climate change has improved. We can now analyze polar ice cores to aid in the reconstruction of sea levels, temperature, and glacial and interglacial phases.

- One well-supported hypothesis suggests that sedentary and socially complex groups emerged in the so-called Early Natufian period, around 15,000 to 13,000 years ago. And these culture changes mapped onto a warming period during the final stages of the last glacial period called the Bølling-Allerød.

- This warmer period began with the end of a very cold period known as the Younger Dryas, the earliest and longest of 3 cold periods that resulted from fairly abrupt climatic changes that took place around 14,500 years ago.

- During this time, the Earth's climate began to shift from a cold glacial environment to a warmer interglacial state. During this transition, temperatures in the Northern Hemisphere rapidly returned to almost glacial conditions in decades.

- Scientists think that Younger Dryas was caused by changes in ocean circulation when there was an influx of fresh cold water from North America into the Atlantic.

- Some scholars believe that the Younger Dryas led to great resource stress and thus triggered a decline in settlement population density and a return to mobility and foraging. The end of the Younger Dryas, then, is associated with the development of large settled villages.

- In the late 1940s, American archaeologist Robert Braidwood proposed an alternative hypothesis, suggesting that Childe's oasis hypothesis was not the most likely scenario, as there were earlier episodes of global warming that had not led to the domestication of plants and animals.

- Other contemporary archaeologists also claim that these large climatic events do not necessarily map onto cultural events and caution against origin hypotheses that associate climate as the only driver for cultivation.

- Another model, proposed by archaeologist David Rindos, invokes a hypothesis based in evolutionary biology. This model suggests that plants and humans coevolved, with the protection of wild plants coming first, leading to domestication.

- Another model, initially proposed by archaeologist Brian Hayden, is called the feasting hypothesis and suggests that agriculture was driven by a desire to display power by throwing feasts to establish social and political dominance.

- Yet other models argue that the beginnings of cultivation are linked with increased sedentism, when populations shifted from being nomadic to a lifestyle where they were more settled. Population growth also led to increased pressure on a limited wild food supply. Proponents of this idea include famous archaeologists Lewis Binford and Kent Flannery.

- These models are only some of the explanations for the origins of agriculture. There is no single consensus on what drove the origins of plant domestication or on where and when agriculture began.

- Up until very recently, scientists believed that agriculture began around 10,000 to 12,000 years ago, with the first evidence of trial plant cultivation. In 2015, however, new evidence emerged that suggests that our ancestors were trying out plant domestication much earlier than anyone imagined—roughly 23,000 years ago.

- We now know that agriculture was invented independently in several locations around the world. While many believe that agriculture begins much earlier, the majority of scientists still believe that the earliest evidence of plant domestication is between 11,000 and 12,000 years ago in the Fertile Crescent, which includes the current countries of Iraq, Syria, Lebanon, Jordan, Palestine, Egypt, and portions of Turkey and Iran.

- Around 11,500 years ago, 8 founder crops—the first known domesticates—appear in several locations in the Fertile Crescent. Founder crops include emmer and einkorn wheat, barley, peas, lentils, chickpeas, flax, and bitter vetch.

- Most scientists agree that wheat was likely the first of these crops to be grown and cultivated on a large scale, although there is some debate about the issue. And it remains unclear whether the first evidence of these plant species indicates deliberate harvesting and replanting, or cultivation.

- Fascinating things were also happening in parts of the world outside of the Fertile Crescent. The earliest evidence of rice consumption, for example, comes from phytoliths, which are microscopic plant fossils. These phytoliths from rice were found in caves in the middle Yangtze River region of China and date to around 12,000 years ago.

- Actual charred remains of rice were found in the Hunan province of China embedded in potsherds and dating to around 10,000 years ago. But there is debate as to whether these rice granules represent domesticated or wild variants. It can be difficult to tease apart plant alteration with direct manipulation of genetic traits.

- Many generations of the first farmers cultivated plots of land by preparing the soil and then removing weeds, and they did this long before most plants showed any physical signs of domestication.

- And it was not just China. There is strong evidence to suggest that early agriculture was also present in India. By 10,000 years ago, we find evidence of domesticated wheat, barley, and jujube.

- In South America, archaeologists have discovered plant remains analyzing phytoliths and the dental calculus, or hardened dental plaque, of skeletons. The data suggests evidence of the domestication of peanuts, potatoes, squash, manioc, arrowroot, and maize. But it is likely that the history of maize begins in Mexico, also around 10,000 years ago.

- It wasn't until around 5000 years ago that we see ancient farming hit North America. Squash, sunflower, and marsh elder are the likely candidates for first domesticated plants in the United States.

Animal Domestication

- Our ancestors starting hunting long ago, possibly as far back as 3 million years ago. But how did we go from hunting wild animals to domesticating them?

- Many scientists now believe that the first animal to be domesticated was the wolf. Researchers who study canine evolution can agree on that but cannot agree on how or the time and location of when it first happened in human history.

- The current thinking on the issue suggests that dogs initially domesticated themselves—around 30,000 to 33,000 years ago. Some research teams suggest that the first dog was European, and some argue for an Asian origin.

- They habituated themselves to humans first, long before we took an active role in the process. The idea is that the tamest wild wolves were able to approach human settlements and consume leftovers.

- They may have then acted as sentries so that humans would tolerate their presence. This version of the wolf story changes the way that many people have thought about animal domestication historically.

- We used to think it was a top-down endeavor, something that humans did with precise intentionality. We linked the idea of dog domestication to a hunter-gatherer with foresight who snatched a wolf puppy and then reared it, raising tamer and tamer wolves.

- But the current mode of thought, according to evolutionary anthropologist Brian Hare, is that wolves played a large role in their own domestication. This makes the relationship between man and his best friend much more interesting and complex than we ever imagined.

- While dogs were not initially domesticated for food, they certainly played a role in the ways in which humans interacted with their foods. Eventually, humans began using dogs to assist with hunting.

- It's likely that cats also initiated contact first. It's thought that they started taking up residence around human camps for a similar reason to dogs—to take advantage of foods scraps. The first cats come on the scene in the Near and Middle East around 10,000 years ago. Cats were probably not very likely to simply stay put. The argument is that they wanted to stay with people.

- This was likely a different scenario for other animals that were domesticated around the same time, namely goats and sheep. They were first domesticated between 11,000 and 12,000 years ago—also from the Near and Middle East.

- The first domesticated pigs show up at this time as well, and it's likely that pigs were independently domesticated in multiple locations around the same time.

- Cows are found a bit later in time, around 10,000 years ago, in India, the Middle East, and North Africa. While preceded by sheep, goats, and pigs, many researchers now think that cattle have actually made the largest impact on human agricultural productivity. They have been used throughout history for various things, including as beasts of burden and for their milk and manure.

- Another animal that is ubiquitous around the world and in its cuisine, much like the cow, is the chicken. It's thought that they, however, were not initially domesticated for food but, rather, for cockfighting. They first appeared around 8000 years ago in India and Southeast Asia and quickly became a source of food, both the birds themselves as well as their eggs.

- The first donkeys were domesticated around 7000 years ago in Egypt. The first horses were domesticated around 6000 years ago in Central Asia.

- The definitive timeline for the domestication of horses is somewhat disputed. They appear in Paleolithic rock art dating to around 20,000 years ago. Many argue that the horses depicted in cave art were unlikely domesticated and were, instead, hunted for meat. Later, when they first appear in Central Asia, they are thought to have been domesticated for transportation, agricultural work, a means of transport for chariot burials, and warfare.

- Other animals originally domesticated for travel include camels, who were domesticated around the same time as horses, with the first evidence appearing in Arabia. Domesticated alpacas and llamas, however, don't appear on the scene until around 4000 to 5000 years ago. Llamas have been used throughout history primarily for wool but also for their meat, hides, and dung.

- Interestingly, of all large mammals on Earth, only 14 of them have been domesticated. Geographer Jared Diamond addresses the question as to why certain animals were domesticated over others by outlining 6 criteria that he claims characterizes all domesticated animals.

1. They have to reach maturity quickly.

2. They cannot be selective or finicky eaters.

3. They have to be able and willing to breed in captive conditions.

4. They cannot have a strong startle response or tendency to flee.

5. They have to be somewhat docile.

6. They must be able to conform to some kind of social hierarchy.

- In addition to Diamond's criteria, scientists also propose 3 major pathways for animal domestication—the different reasons why humans would desire to domesticate an animal.

  1. Some animals (including dogs, cats, chickens, and maybe pigs) were adapted to a human niche.

  2. Some animals (including sheep, goats, and cattle) may have first been prey animals.

  3. Some animals (including horses, donkeys, and camels) were possibly first targeted for draft and nonfood or labor resources.

- Some animals were used exclusively for meat, such as sheep, pigs, goats, and chickens. Some were used for meat and transportation or plowing, such as cows, donkeys, camels, and llamas. Some were used for protection, such as dogs, or pest control, such as cats. Whatever the use, domesticated animals were a game changer in human history.

Suggested Reading

Diamond, *Guns, Germs, and Steel*.
Hanson, *The Triumph of Seeds*.

Questions

1. Approximately when in human history did we first begin domesticating plants and animals?

2. What are the 8 founder crops that are considered to be the first-known plant domesticates?

LECTURE
9

THE CHANGING
DISEASE-SCAPE

When most people think about the advent of agriculture, they think about changes in food economy and social structure but don't think about the consequential changes in population growth and what that meant for disease patterns. Scientists call this the epidemiological transition. This model argues that from the time agriculture became ubiquitous around the world, roughly 10,000 years ago, there have been 3 major disease transitions that have greatly affected humanity, the first of which occurred with the advent of agriculture. This first shift in the landscape of disease, or disease-scape, was tethered to the domestication of plants and animals.

Parasites

- When people became sedentary and began producing and storing their food, this led to population growth. This was because the time between pregnancies could be shortened due to more energy in the diet, which led to higher fertility.

- But this higher fertility was not sustainable, because mortality was also high. Life expectancy was also low and variable, with some estimates putting it between 20 and 40 years.

- One of the reasons that mortality was so high is because people were coming into contact with new disease vectors. Now people were living in much closer quarters with one another, creating the perfect environment for disease transmission.

- They were also now living with their domesticated animals, which greatly increased the transmission of zoonotic diseases, which are diseases that can be caused by viruses, bacteria, or parasites and are spread between animals and humans.

- When our ancestors were hunting and gathering, the rates of infectious disease were low, but they likely had high rates of parasitic infections. While there is debate as to the extent to which our ancestral foragers suffered from these infections, many scientists believe that our immune systems may have evolved to tolerate such microorganisms.

- This idea that we coevolved with many of these microbes is called the old friends hypothesis. It's based on the idea that we didn't take our evolutionary journey on our own. It's thought that we had little passengers come with us. These included many different species, but one is lice.

- While lice can infect many different animals, humans have proven to be a fantastic home. We can harbor multiple species of lice. And scientists have identified many different types—head lice, body hair lice, and clothing lice—searching for clues as to how lice might tell us something about human evolution.

- We can track milestones in human evolution by looking to our hitchhiking friends. Some researchers who study the lice genome

have argued that we can trace the splitting of species and map this onto which species of early human they targeted.

- They argue that one group likely evolved onto *Homo erectus*, who lived from around 2 million years ago to probably about 70,000 years ago. Another group likely evolved onto Neanderthals, who lived in Eurasia from around 300,000 years ago to about 30,000 years ago.

- But at some point in history, these separate species encountered one another again—and reunited. Now humans are the hosts to all 3 of the original types of lice.

- It turns out that lice might not be all that bad for us. Surprisingly, they might even carry a few benefits. Researchers have found that lice might help our immune system to function and reduce the risk of things like allergies.

- This idea that microorganisms can be beneficial doesn't stop with lice. Parasitic worms might also be beneficial—in the right circumstances. Intestinal worms are called helminths. Many helminths are linked with severe infection, and sometimes even death. But there are many helminth species that don't cause any direct harm and might even help us.

- Like lice, helminths might help protect against allergies and autoimmune conditions. Some cutting-edge treatments of multiple sclerosis, Crohn's disease, and irritable bowel syndrome involve the controlled use of helminths.

- Mutualistic intestinal parasites have been a part of our environment and the ecosystem of our body for millions of years. During our coevolution, they became an integral part of our immune function. They help stimulate our body to build networks of immune cells that can act to decrease general inflammation. And they do this without hurting our immune system's ability to respond to actual danger or disease.

- The link between the changing disease-scape in our past maps onto the changing nutritional landscape. When we shifted to agriculture all around the world, about 10,000 years ago, it's likely that these types of parasites became more communicable. They did so because a more sedentary lifestyle was adopted—one that involved living in permanent indoor structures.

The Transmission of Zoonotic Diseases

- Moving beyond parasites, the much more nefarious situation during the Neolithic period was the transmission of zoonotic diseases. Our history with zoonotic diseases has deep evolutionary origins.

- Some of the most common zoonotic diseases are Lyme disease, West Nile virus, malaria, salmonella, and *E. coli*. Lyme disease is transmitted via ticks, whereas West Nile virus and malaria are transmitted via mosquitoes. Salmonella and *E. coli*, on the other hand, are foodborne illnesses.

- There are also other zoonotic diseases that likely hit our early ancestors pretty hard. Some of these likely led to the high mortality rates that we see during the first epidemiological transition. They included typhus, typhoid, and schistosomiasis.

- Typhus, while commonly confused with typhoid, is actually caused by an entirely different genera of bacteria. Typhus is transmitted to humans via external parasites, such as ticks, fleas, and lice. Thanks to effective vaccination, only a few areas of epidemic typhus still exist today.

- Typhoid, or typhoid fever, is a bacterial infection from species from the genus *Salmonella*. Historically, typhoid first affected cattle, sheep, pigs, and chickens and then was transmitted to humans. Now, *Salmonella typhi*, the specific bacterium responsible for typhoid, is transmitted from person to person. In the United States, typhoid rates are comparatively low, but it is still very common in the developing world.

- Schistosomiasis, also known as bilharzia, is a potentially damaging disease that is caused by parasitic worms. About 200 million people a year in the world suffer from bilharzia, which is caused by parasites found in freshwater snails.

Nutritional Deficiencies

- In addition to the transmission of these zoonotic diseases, the transition to agriculture also came with increased nutritional deficiencies. During a time of population growth, there was a decline in health. This is not only linked with disease vectors but is also associated with declines in nutrition.

- Bioarchaeologists study every aspect of skeletons. The type of bioarchaeologist who specializes in studying disease and trauma is called a paleopathologist, one who studies ancient patterns of disease.

- Many nutritional deficiencies can be identified by looking at skeletal material. By analyzing the bones of early farmers, paleopathologists argue that the rates of malnutrition and iron-deficiency anemia are much higher than their foraging predecessors.

- The reasons that malnutrition might have been higher are debated, but it's likely due to the fact that early farmers were reliant on a handful of crops that might have been nutritionally deficient. This is very different from the varied and seasonal diet that foragers were consuming.

- In addition, because the number of crops was limited (at least during the early stages of agriculture), starvation was a threat. If one crop failed, it could have dire consequences. Couple this with sedentism and increased vectors for disease and it makes sense why mortality was so high and life expectancy was so short.

- An example comes from the archeological site of Dickson Mounds, a Native American settlement site in Illinois dating to around 1000 years ago. This site represents a transitional phase where the residents were moving from hunting and gathering to agriculture. The fact that this transition is documented has allowed bioarchaeologists to determine the health of the residents before and after domestication.

- Researchers have analyzed bone growth, enamel development, and mortality patterns and have determined that the adoption of agriculture came with a heavy price. Major declines in health were found. Compared to the hunter-gatherers before them, the farmers' skeletons at Dickson Mounds had a significant increase in iron-deficiency anemia and degenerative spinal conditions, such as arthritis.

- Children between the ages of 5 and 10 years old were particularly susceptible to underdeveloped early leg growth. This meant that they had shorter legs, with shorter and narrower bones.

- Declines in health also extended to the mouth. Domestication appears to map onto the expansion of bacteria found in dental plaque, which contains the specific type of bacteria linked with the development of cavities, or dental caries, and periodontal disease.

- Up until very recently, the dominating opinion was that cavities formed as tooth enamel and dentin were demineralized by acids produced from plaque bacteria during the fermentation of carbohydrates.

- Research over the past several decades, however, is challenging this assumption. Many scientists now argue that the mechanisms of cariogenesis, or how dental caries are developed, are not so easy to pinpoint.

- Scientists in this field of oral health research argue that other factors might be at play, including one's oral microbiome (the specific ecosystem of bacteria that live in our mouths), diet composition (what you eat and how often), genetic susceptibility, and your mother's oral health when she was pregnant with you.

- Dental diseases, in general, are particularly important to bioarchaeologists because teeth are resistant to degradation and, like bones, show up in the archaeological record. They also contain valuable information about health and dietary patterns.

- While very common today, cavities have only been documented in about 2% of observed populations from the Paleolithic and Mesolithic periods, from approximately 2.5 million years ago to around 10,000 years ago—before the advent of agriculture.

- Many bioarchaeologists link the onset and intensification of agriculture to increased rates of dental disease. The idea is that there's an evolutionary mismatch between the oral biology that was associated with the adoption of domestication and the dietary environment in which our teeth and gums evolved.

- One of the exceptions to this bioarchaeological rule, however, has tended to be prehistoric rice agriculturalists. The thought is that this is because their starchy staple was non-cariogenic, meaning a food that's typically not associated with cavity creation as other starchy staples are.

- While the narrative that declining oral health maps onto the origins of plant domestication is well ensconced in the literature, this assumption is now being challenged. As more studies of living populations outside of the postindustrialized West are conducted, we are learning more about what a transition away from foraging looks like in real time.

- For example, research by Alyssa Crittenden and Peter Ungar has shown that despite differing diets, Hadza foragers living in each of their residential locales, from bush to village, showed evidence of caries, periodontal disease, and a lot of wear on their teeth. But there were significant sex differences that mapped onto location differences.

- Women residing in the bush had the best oral health overall, whereas men residing in the bush had the worst oral health. Women living in the village, however, had worse teeth compared to the men living in the bush. The differences most likely come down to diet and lifestyle choices.

- Hadza women in the bush tend to eat more fibrous tubers, which are covered with grit, which might act to clean the teeth of biofilm, or plaque, that builds up to create cavities. In addition, men smoke much more tobacco than women, and smoking leads to higher rates of caries and periodontal disease.

Suggested Reading

Diamond, *Guns, Germs, and Steel*.
Rook, ed., *The Hygiene Hypothesis and Darwinian Medicine*.

Questions

1. Why is the first epidemiological transition important, and how does it map onto the origins of agriculture?

2. What are some of the diseases that are associated with the domestication of animals?

HOW FOODS
SPREAD AROUND
THE WORLD

M ost people regularly consider the contents of their diets, but few people regularly consider where their food is coming from. And even less frequently do they think about the historic, cultural, and geopolitical forces that have moved food around the globe for thousands of years. In this lecture, by taking a look at the migration of a few foods, you will appreciate how the global food system came to be.

Delocalization

- Our foraging ancestors were limited in the foods that they could consume. They were limited by availability, as they could only access and consume foods that were indigenous to the region in which they were living. They were also tethered to seasonality, just like the plants and animals that they consumed. This meant a healthy and likely well-balanced diet, but one that was ecologically variable and geographically dependent.

- When our ancestors began the domestication process, this all changed. They were still limited to foods that could be cultivated or raised locally, but they exercised choice. They could now target specific foods or specific traits that they wanted to cultivate.

- Once domestication was in full swing, foods started being exchanged. By the time the 13th century started, large-scale trade was underway, and new foods were being disseminated throughout the world.

- As a direct result of migration and trade, many of the foods that we now associate with particular cuisines actually originated far away from where they were domesticated.

- When nutritional anthropologists and other social scientists study the ways in which patterns of food consumption and culture interact, they discuss a concept called delocalization, which is a process by which increasing amounts of a population or community's diet comes from an increasing distance away from that population or community. It can be seen as a shift from local autonomy to a dependence on a global system of trade, production, and politics.

- Before World War II, many food systems around the world were still very localized. The United States, like other countries in the postindustrialized West, was a bit different. Thanks to efficient national railway systems, foods produced on one side of the country could be easily distributed throughout the nation.

- Closely linked with the idea of delocalization is the idea of food commoditization, or treating food and nutrition as a market economy. Many nutrition researchers argue that while delocalization does not necessarily map onto increased malnutrition and food insecurity, it does mean that access to adequate nutrition might be increasingly difficult.

- And this process of delocalization goes back deep in time. In fact, it's the main characteristic of the global diet that we know of today.

Bananas

- Bananas were first domesticated approximately 8000 years ago, with the earliest evidence coming from Southeast Asia and surrounding areas, such as Papua New Guinea and the South Pacific. Researchers find it difficult to trace the precise migration of the banana because it was independently domesticated in several different regions around the same time.

- Bananas then dispersed widely from New Guinea and the Philippines, traveling across the Tropics in all directions and to the rest of the world.

- By the 1200s, bananas were in North Africa and Europe and throughout Asia. And they were not simply grown for human consumption. Japanese cultivators, for example, grew varietals that were specifically used for textiles and other fabrics.

- By the 15th century, sailors from Portugal were growing the crop throughout Brazil. From there, it spread to the sugar plantations of the New World and the Caribbean. By the turn of the 20th century, the banana had completely shifted from being a local food to a global commodity.

- Bananas were, and are, a wonderful nonseasonal crop. This is why we can purchase a banana all year long and why they're a staple food for many populations in Africa, Asia, South and Central America, and the Pacific Islands.

- While there are about 50 different species of banana that can be planted, only one variety dominates the world market: Cavendish. More than 100 billion bananas are now consumed annually all around the world.

Apples

- The original wild ancestor of the apple hails from the mountains of Central Asia. Apples are a member of the Rosaceae, or rose family, which they share with other fruits, such as pears, peaches, plums, strawberries, cherries, and raspberries. They made it to North America in the 17th century, when Reverend William Blaxton planted the first trees in Boston.

- There are about 2000 different apple varieties, which is great for the fruit as a species but tricky for cultivators. John Chapman, also called Johnny Appleseed, was a cultivator who was responsible for bringing apples to Indiana, Illinois, Ohio, Pennsylvania, and West Virginia. The main varieties of apple that he planted were small, tart, green apples.

Potatoes

- While some associate the potato with Ireland and others with the United States, it actually likely comes from South America.

- Humans have a long evolutionary relationship with tubers. Our foraging ancestors were targeting tubers as far back as 2 million years ago.

- But the first domesticated tuber didn't come on the scene until around 10,000 years ago with the beginnings of agriculture. Although there is debate as to where and when the first domesticated potato appeared, many believe that it's from the Andes region of South America, dating to as early as 8000 years ago.

- The potato is part of the nightshade family, whose other members include eggplants, tomatoes, peppers, and tomatillos.

- In the High Plains, the Andean and Bolivian plateaus, potatoes were a staple crop. They're considered to be one of the central foods in the cuisine of Inca society.

- The height of the Inca empire was from around 1438 to 1533, the center of which was located in the current-day countries of Bolivia, Colombia, Ecuador, and Peru. The Incas developed resilient breeds of potatoes—and other crops, such as corn and quinoa. These crops fared very well on the high plateaus.

- Potatoes left the Andes region after the fall of the Inca empire and began their long trek around the world. By the 1500s, sailors from

Spain were known to have begun planting potatoes in their home gardens. From Spain, the potato traveled slowly to Europe.

- The first evidence of potatoes in Ireland was around 1559, and by the year 1600, it had taken root in Spain, Portugal, Italy, Austria, Belgium, Holland, France, Switzerland, England, and Germany.

- Potatoes arrived in the United States, then the British colonies, in the 1600s—but didn't catch on as a major crop until the late 1800s.

Tomatoes

- The tomato started its journey in Central and South America thousands of years ago. Tomatoes are members of the nightshade family, which also includes many poisonous plants. They are technically a fruit, but the question of whether a tomato is a vegetable or a fruit dates back to the 19th century.

- While the wild species of tomato are native to the Andes region of South America, they reached Mesoamerica likely by 2500 years ago. Archaeologists don't know how the tomato traveled from the Andean region—whether it was due to intentional transportation by people or unintentional transportation by water, wind, or migrating birds.

- The first domesticated tomato likely came from Mexico. Scientists have had a difficult time finding evidence of the plant from archaeological remains, including coprolites (fossilized feces). The reason for this, they argue, is that people were largely consuming tomatoes by grinding them up for use in sauces, stews, and salsas, which makes it difficult to identify seeds.

- By the time Spaniards arrived in Mexico in 1519, the tomato was used in many dishes that were sold on streets and in markets. Those were dishes that the Spaniards enjoyed—and wrote home about.

- There is some debate as to the identity of the first person to introduce the tomato to Europe. Some believe that Christopher Columbus might have taken back some samples of the fruit as early as 1493. Others argue that it was conquistador Hernán Cortéz, who took samples back to Spain in 1521 after he conquered the Aztec city of Tenochtitlán, modern-day Mexico City.

- Tomatoes first show up in Italy around 1540, but it wasn't until the late 1700s that tomatoes started appearing in dishes listed in Italian cookbooks.

- The earliest reference to tomatoes in North America was not until the early 1700s, when herbalist William Salmon reported seeing them in South Carolina.

- Today, tomatoes are popular all around the world—in all varieties. These include heirloom, cherry, Roma, and beefsteak tomatoes. More than 1.5 billion tons of tomatoes are produced annually for commercial consumption around the world.

Corn

- Another plant that is produced in massive quantities for global consumption is corn. Corn is arguably one of most important crops in the world—both historically and today. In the United States, when people say "corn," they mean maize. But in other countries, the word can refer to different plant species.

- Maize corn originated in Mexico around 10,000 years ago. It started out as a tall tropical grass, called teosinte, which does not look much like the corn stalks that we are used to.

- The earliest directly dated maize cobs were found in the Mexican highlands. Cobs were found in Tehuacán and Oaxaca in the 1960s, but dating methods were not yet available, so we had no direct dates until the early 2000s. Archaeologists Kent Flannery and Dolores Piperno have now dated the cobs to about 6250 years ago.

- Evidence of early maize has also been found in the Andean region of Peru. Archaeologist Jonathan Haas and colleagues discovered microscopic evidence in soil, on stone tools, and in coprolites that suggests that Peruvians were growing and eating corn 5000 years ago.

- Data from Peru and Mexico suggest that dozens of different types of maize were used, some for consumption (such as beer and flour) and some for other uses (such as textile dyes).

- Many historians believe that Christopher Columbus was the first person to take corn back to Europe. But scientists argue that corn was likely primarily dispersed by the diffusion of seeds on trade routes and that is how it made the trek out of Mexico.

- By 3000 years ago, corn was being consumed by Native Americans in the Southwest and, by around 2000 years ago, by Native Americans in the Eastern United States. Maize is now a major staple all around the world and a primary nutrition source for much of the continent of Africa as well as North America.

Suggested Reading

Kiple, ed., *The Cambridge World History of Food*.
Koeppel, *Banana*.

Questions

1. How is the concept of delocalization linked to the migration of foods?

2. What is an example of a food that is consumed all around the world and embodies delocalization?

THE HISTORY OF THE SPICE TRADE

Culinarily, spices are used to flavor, color, and preserve food. Botanically, spices are extracted from bark, roots, gums, seeds, or flower buds. Chemically, they're known for their oleoresins, which are the naturally occurring combinations of oils and resins that can be extracted from the plant in question. Historically, spices are one of the largest catalysts for global trade and exploration. They were very valuable—which was largely a product of where they originated and how difficult they were to obtain. It is this rich narrative of spices that will be addressed in this lecture.

The History of Spices

- The history of spices begins in the mid- to late 15th century, which saw the beginning of the so-called European age of discovery, characterized by extensive overseas exploration on the part of Europeans.

- Marco Polo, the famous Venetian-born merchant who sailed the seas in 1292, sailed through the China Sea and the Indian Ocean and was the first to write about the famous Spice Islands—the Maluku Islands—west of New Guinea. The Maluku Islands are a series of 11 small volcanic islands that early geographers called "the country where the spices grow."

- But it wasn't until more than 100 years later that the first successful search for the Spice Islands would commence. A key player in the birth of the age of exploration was Henry the Navigator, the third child of the Portuguese King John I and his wife, Queen Philippa, sister to King Henry the IV of England.

- In 1415, King John and his sons captured the port town of Ceuta, in northern Morocco. This was a critical step in the formation of the Portuguese sailing empire as well as the growth of European colonial expansion. After this time, Henry began traveling the coast of Africa, encountering new territories previously unknown to European trade routes.

- The political landscape changed during the mid-1400s, and less emphasis was placed on exploring Africa. When King Manuel ascended to the Portuguese throne in 1495, however, he rejuvenated an abandoned plan to open the sea route to Asia. This would mean opening up trade routes with India.

- Vasco da Gama's first voyage to India was in 1497, and Portugal held a monopoly on trade with Asia for some time. It wasn't until almost 100 years later that other European countries, such as England and France, were able to challenge Portugal's naval supremacy. And it was da Gama who reached India's spice routes first—much to Christopher Columbus's chagrin.

- Columbus's voyage was organized with the intention of capturing the legendary Indian spice routes. His first trip to India was actually to American shores. He continued with multiple voyages, claiming "India" with each new landfall, and the myth that America was the land of spices was compelling to leaders and seafarers of the day. It was not until almost 100 years after Columbus first set sail for the "Indies" that this myth was finally dispelled.

- Interestingly, it wasn't until the Spanish crown prepared another voyage, this time with Ferdinand Magellan at the helm, that the first spice route to Asia was actually created. Magellan's plan was not altogether different than the plan Columbus had originally proposed.

- The one key difference is that Magellan knew that North America was blocking his passage. So, he planned a route that would go south—past South America—and then west.

- His expedition to the East Indies in 1519 was the first circumnavigation of the Earth. Magellan not only changed seafaring history, but also our culinary lives, forever.

- By the late 1500s, the Dutch were ready to make their move into the international spice trade. Dutch merchants, such as Cornelis de Houtman, were also spice hunters.

- By the time the Dutch began dominating the spice trade in the early 1600s, spices were already the established top market trade item in the world. The United East Indian Company, known colloquially in England as the Dutch East India Company, began a world-famous 21-year monopoly on the spice trade, starting in 1602.

- All of these explorers were all spice seekers—and there were many others. They all became key players in the age of discovery, but their primary motivation was to capture the spice routes.

- While there are hundreds of different types of spices, only a few were the most critically important when the spice routes opened: pepper, ginger, cloves, cinnamon, and nutmeg.

Pepper

- Black pepper comes from a flowering vine. The fruits, called peppercorns, are dried and ground up to create the pepper that we use. There are many other varieties, including white, green, red, and orange, but black pepper is the most famous in history. Pepper is argued to be the king of the spices and may be the most widely used spice in the world.

- Pepper originates from the Malabar Coast in India. From here, it traveled to the rest of Southcoast Asia. It is used widely, and for many purposes, beyond its value as a pungent spice. It was found in the nose of Egyptian King Ramses II as part his embalming procedure, and it is still considered to be an integral part of Ayurvedic medicine today.

- Pepper first makes an appearance in history around 3500 years ago, when it was listed in the famous Ebers papyrus, an Egyptian medical papyrus that is thought to have been copied from even earlier texts.

- Around 2000 years ago, when Rome captured Egypt, the pepper trade fell under Roman control, and pepper graced many Roman dinner tables. It appears in multiple types of historical documents, including Roman textbooks of the day, and archaeological data confirms the widespread use.

- Around 1180, King Henry II of England created the Pepperer's Guild, the first mercantile guild to be recorded in London.

- In 1280, Marco Polo described the pepper growing in Java.

- In 1600, the British East India Company was established, specifically to start trading pepper. While there was some back and forth between the British and the Dutch, by 1800, the British had become the dominant power in the pepper trade. Around 1795 or 1800, Americans entered into the business of pepper.

- During its heyday, pepper was used as valuable currency. While other spices were more profitable, such as nutmeg and cloves, pepper was used in much greater quantities.

- Today, the world's largest producer of pepper is Vietnam, followed by India, Indonesia, and Brazil. Pepper is used in cuisines all around the world and is also currently being used medicinally, as it has been throughout history. It has antibacterial properties, and some research suggests that it might be a good anti-ulcerative or anti-inflammatory substance.

Ginger

- Ginger, a very common ingredient in Asian cuisine, has long been touted as a remedy for nausea and motion sickness.

- The ginger that we are familiar with is actually the underground rhizome, or underground stem and root segments, of the ginger plant. It can be eaten fresh, powdered, pickled, or candied or eaten as a spice, oil, juice, wine, or beer. Ginger might be one of the world's oldest spices.

- It originated in Southeast Asia and today is grown commercially in India, China, Indonesia, Nigeria, the Philippines, Thailand, and Brazil.

Cloves

- Like pepper, cloves are native to the Maluku Islands in Indonesia. They are common to the cuisines of countries in Asia, Africa, and the Near and Middle East. Outside of culinary uses, cloves have also been long used in Ayurvedic medicine.

- Cloves are actually the dried and unripe flower buds of a tree from the Myrtle family. The chemical component that is responsible for the distinct flavor and scent that are associated with cloves is called eugenol.

- Some Ayurvedic and traditional Chinese medicine health practitioners have argued that the presence of eugenol makes

clove oil a good remedy for toothaches or as an antihelminthic, an antiparasitic that might dispel digestive worms. The U.S. Food and Drug Administration, however, has not approved clove oil for these uses.

- Cloves are also used to make a type of cigarette that combines tobacco and ground clove powder. They are thought to be one of the world's first breath mints.

- While once grown exclusively in Indonesia, cloves are now also grown in Madagascar, Tanzania, Comoros, and Sri Lanka.

- Zanzibar, an island off of East Africa, is where cloves are produced in Tanzania—and it has a dark history with the production of the spice. By the turn of the 19th century, Zanzibar was one of the world's top clove producers.

- First under Portuguese control for almost 200 years, Zanzibar then fell under control of Oman. The Omani developed an economy of trade crops, where the Arabs were the ruling elite and the local Bantu-speaking Africans provided all of the labor.

- The 3 pillars of commerce for the Omani-run Zanzibar were spices, centered on cloves, ivory, and slaves. The cultivation of cloves on the large plantations was done exclusively by slave labor.

- The Spice Islands of the 21st century are now the Zanzibar archipelago, and a large population of residents on these islands depends on the clove harvest for their livelihood.

Nutmeg

- Nutmeg is a seed of an evergreen tree that is also native to the Maluku Islands of Indonesia. Nutmeg was thought to be a commodity by Muslim sailors from the ancient port of Basra, located between Kuwait and Iran.

- In 1621, the Dutch East India Company had its eyes set on nutmeg. They waged a catastrophic attack on residents of the Banda Islands, part of the Maluku Islands, that left only 1000 people alive out of a population of 15,000. The British also secured a colony on a nearby island so that they, too, could export nutmeg.

- Today, the world's top producers are Indonesia, Guatemala, India, Zanzibar, and Grenada. In addition to its wide use as a spice, nutmeg also has a history of being used for medicinal purposes and as an aphrodisiac. Long used in traditional Chinese and Ayurvedic medicine, nutmeg has been argued to be a remedy for inflammation and digestive issues as well as an antifungal and antioxidant.

Cinnamon

- Cinnamon, also with origins in Asia, comes from the bark of trees from the *Cinnamomum* genus, a type of laurel tree. Some of the oldest evidence of cinnamon consumption comes from Israel. Archaeologists analyzed 10 flasks and found residue of cinnamaldehyde, a major component of cinnamon that is associated with its distinct flavor.

- This data provides tantalizing evidence that long-distance spice trade routes existed 3000 years ago. The argument is that to obtain cinnamon, people living in the Levant would have had to engage in trade that extended well beyond the edge of their known world.

- Even earlier evidence, from around 3500 years ago, suggests that ancient Egyptians were using cinnamon as part of the embalming process, much like pepper. It was also mentioned in Sanskrit documents from around this time.

- Outside of Europe, merchants from Arabic-speaking regions—the Middle East and North Africa—had a monopoly on cinnamon trade until the 16th century.

- Around 1518, Portuguese sailors had discovered cinnamon in Sri Lanka. Roughly 100 years later, the Dutch had taken over this region and held a monopoly on the cinnamon trade for the next 150 years. It was such a highly valued spice that it was used as currency.

- Today, cinnamon is the second most popular spice, after black pepper, in the United States and Europe.

- The world grows 2 different types of cinnamon: the more expensive Ceylon cinnamon, produced in Sri Lanka, and the more common cassia cinnamon, which hails from trees in southern China. Some tantalizing research has suggested that Ceylon cinnamon might lower blood sugar in people with diabetes. It may also contain chemicals that help fight against fungal and bacterial infections. Some exciting research with animal models also suggests that it might help cognitive function with Alzheimer's.

Suggested Reading

Czarra, *Spices*.

Questions

1. How does the history of the spice trade map onto the European age of discovery?

2. What is the history of the Dutch East India Company and the spice trade?

LECTURE
12

HOW SUGAR
AND SALT SHAPED
WORLD HISTORY

Both sugar and salt have a fascinating tale to tell, and one that affects each of us on a daily basis. Both salt and sugar influence our daily lives. They have not only been key commodities throughout history but have also played large roles in food production around the world and in global health. Fortunes have been made and destroyed by sugar and salt, and wars have been waged—all because of the desire to control access to sweetness and saltiness.

Sugar

- Sugar is consumed all around us every day. From the granulated variety that we sprinkle into our morning coffee, to the cane that people all around the world routinely chew on, to the sweet carbonated soft drinks that have become ubiquitous with American culture.

- What we call sugar is actually a carbohydrate. There are many different types of sugar. Simple sugars, for example, are called monosaccharides and include glucose, fructose, and galactose. Granulated sugar, what most of us think of when we think of sugar, is sucrose, a disaccharide. There are other disaccharides, such as maltose and lactose (the sugar in milk).

- Sugars are found in almost all plant foods but only exist in adequate concentrations for extraction in some plants, mainly sugarcane and the sugar beet. Sugarcane (from the genus *Saccharum*) consists of several different species of tall fibrous grasses that grow in tropical climates.

- The birthplace of domesticated sugarcane is thought to be in New Guinea close to 10,000 years ago with the agricultural

revolution. It was then carried to the Philippines, China, India, and Indonesia—although some scholars think that Indonesia might be an independent place of origin.

- At first, sugar was processed manually, by chewing on the cane stalk. It wasn't until around 1700 years ago that sugarcane was made portable. This likely first happened in India.

- The earliest production centers of sugar were thought to be located in Pakistan and Iran. Many sugar historians now believe that sugar didn't reach Europe until the Crusades, medieval military campaigns during the 11th and 15th centuries.

- During this time, many warriors traveled from Europe to the Holy Lands, returning with very expensive and highly valuable "sweet salt." In the right climates, sugar began being produced, largely as a product of Arab expansion.

- Sites of production included Sicily, Cypress, Malta, and Spain. Some argue that sugar actually reached Venice before the Crusades and then began being exported north.

- It wasn't until the 1390s that an efficient sugar press was invented. Both Portugal and Spain wanted to increase production, and in both countries, a growing demand for sugar was met with the use of slave labor.

- Some historians argue that this practice was borrowed from the sugar plantations that were seen in the Middle East during the Crusades. And it was Spain, who sent Christopher Columbus to the New World, that was responsible for sugar reaching the shores of the Americas. It is thought that Columbus first brought sugar with him in 1493.

- It was then subsequently grown in great quantities in Santo Domingo, in present-day Dominican Republic. This city was founded in 1496 by Christopher Columbus's younger brother, mapmaker Bartholomew Columbus.

- In 1501, Spanish monarchs Ferdinand and Isabella granted the colonists permission to import African slaves. They began arriving in Santo Domingo in 1503, and the first fully operational sugar mill opened around 1515.

- Yet this burgeoning Spanish-American industry, which pioneered sugarcane production, sugar making, and slave labor, did not become the world's leader in the sugar industry.

- Within a century, the Western world's largest sugar producers were the Portuguese, who grew their sugar in Brazil, and the French and the British, with assistance from the Dutch.

- After 1625, the Dutch began transporting sugarcane from South America to the Caribbean islands. Its worth was often compared to highly valuable commodities, such as spices and pearls. By 1750, sugar was considered to be the most valuable commodity in Europe.

- As Europeans established more sugar plantations all around the Caribbean, prices fell. During the 18th century, Europe's taste for sweetness was fixed. All levels of society could now enjoy sugar.

- In World War I in Britain, sugar was rationed, starting in 1918, followed by other staples, such as meat, butter, and gasoline. In America, which didn't enter that war until late in the game, voluntary rationing was encouraged so that supplies could be sent to the people abroad.

- During World War II, governments issued ration books, which contained coupons that shopkeepers cut out or signed when people bought food. The idea was to make sure that everybody got a fair share of the food available.

- The fear was that as food and other items became scarcer, prices would rise and only rich people would be able to buy them. There was also a danger that some people might hoard items, leaving none for others.

- In World War II, sugar was the first article to be rationed in the United States. By the spring of 1942, Americans were unable to purchase sugar without government-issued food coupons. The war with Japan had cut off U.S. imports from the Philippines, and cargo ships from Hawaii were diverted for military purposes.

- The nation's supply of sugar was quickly reduced by more than a third. To prevent hoarding and skyrocketing prices, the Office of Price Administration issued 123 million copies of War Ration Book One, which contained stamps that could be used to purchase sugar. No sugar could legally be bought without stamps.

- By the end of the war, restrictions on processed foods and other goods, such as gasoline and fuel oil, were lifted, but the rationing of sugar remained in effect until 1947, 2 years after the war had ended.

- In World War II, Britain experienced 14 years of rationing, from 1940 until 1954, 9 years after the end of the war. Pregnant women and children under 16 had a different-color ration book and were allotted more fruit, meat, milk, and eggs than others.

- Rationing in Germany was even more severe and with more inequality, as Jews and Poles received starvation rations while others did quite well. On the black market, almost anything was available for those who could afford to pay for it. Theft of rationing stamps or counterfeiting them was a criminal offense, however, and violators could end up in detention at a forced labor camp. As the war went on, it might even mean a death sentence.

- Sugar has also been rationed in peacetime. It was rationed in Britain in 1974 after Caribbean producers began selling to the more lucrative United States market. In Poland, sugar was rationed in 1952 and again from 1976 to 1985. In Israel, under a regime of austerity, sugar rationing was in effect from 1949 to 1959.

- It's estimated that the average American consumes about 20 teaspoons a day, which translates into more than 66 pounds a year. The American Heart Association recently added its voice to the many warnings against consuming too much sugar. Many endocrinologists and medical professionals claim that sugar is toxic.

Salt

- Salt is so easily acquired today, and so inexpensive, that we often forget that until about 100 years ago, it was one of the most sought-after items in the world.

- Salt is a mineral that is composed of mostly sodium chloride. Sodium is needed by most animals to sustain life, and salt is involved in regulating fluid balance in the body. It also helps the digestive system absorb nutrients. Salt is one of the 5 main tastes, along with sweet, sour, bitter, and umami (savoriness).

- The first salt dates to nearly 10,000 years ago. Some scholars believe that it was first processed in China, whereas others believe it may have been Romania. Processing sites dating to roughly the same time period, around 8000 years ago, have been found in both locations. It was also a valued commodity to many other ancient civilizations, including the Greeks, Romans, Byzantines, Hittites, and Egyptians.

- Salt was an incredibly valuable additive because it helped preserve food. This made it a highly sought-after commodity. It was carried along prehistoric trade routes, called salt roads. Caravans traveling along the salt roads consisting of massive caravans traveling over incredible distances.

- One of the most famous salt markets of the Old World was Timbuktu, a city located in the West African country of Mali. It was originally a seasonal settlement but, over time, became a flourishing center of trade.

- Early in the 12th century, it became a permanent settlement. After the salt roads and other trade routes shifted in its favor, it became one of the epicenters of trade in gold, ivory, slaves, and salt.

- Salt was integral in Chinese history. It was not only a stable source of revenue for the government but also a driver of technological change. The Chinese government was one of the first to impose salt taxes, greatly propelling their economic development forward.

- China houses at least 5 different types of salt: sea salt, lake salt, earth salt, rock salt, and well salt (housed in deep subterranean pools).

- The first written record of salt production in China dates to around 800 B.C., or around 2800 years ago. This document describes production and trade of sea salt that occurred 1000 years before the writing of the book. It describes a then-ancient method in which seawater was placed into clay vessels and boiled until only salt crystals remained.

- Another ancient method of production was to boil brine in iron pans, a method that would become the leading means for production for the following 2000 years. It was discovered around 252 B.C. that brine seeped up from underground sources. It was right around this time that the first drilling of brine wells occurred.

- Outside of China, salt also played a large role in cultural customs, cuisines, and economy. Ancient Egypt, for example, made great use of salt. It has been found in tombs, in remains of food, and as funeral offerings. Historians believe that the ancient Egyptians were some of the first to cure meat and fish with salt.

- Salt was, and still is, important in the religious practices of some cultures. There are more than 30 direct references to the use of salt in the Bible. Salt was very important to both ancient Hebrews and people of Jewish faith today. It is thought by many religions that evil spirits avoid salt. Salt is also important in religious rituals in Buddhism, Hinduism, and Jainism.

- Outside of religious practices, there are also other non-dietary uses of salt. In fact, the salt industry claims that there are more than 14,000 non-dietary uses of salt, ranging from pharmaceutical production to dying textiles.

- Today, only about 6% of the salt that is manufactured globally is used in food. The remainder gets used to deice highways, in water-conditioning processes, in agriculture, and the vast majority—almost 70%—for industrial processes.

- Salt is used to produce chlorine and lye, which are used to produce plastic. It's also used in the production of glycerine, soap, and synthetic rubber and in the process of firing ceramics.

- The leading salt producers in the world today are China (which produces about 23% of the world's salt supply), the United States (about 15%), India (about 9%), and Germany (about 7%). The remainder is produced all over the world, largely for domestic consumption in the country where it is collected and processed.

- Two of the largest salt corporations in the United States are American Rock Salt and Morton. American Rock Salt is based out of New York State and is the largest operating salt mine in the United States, producing up to 18,000 tons a day. Morton Salt is based in Chicago but mines salt all around the world.

- Morton is still the leading brand in America, but it's having a more difficult time selling its product as a health product today. While we do have a physiological need for salt in our diet, many medical professionals now argue that most Americans might be getting way too much of it.

- Too much salt can eventually lead to high blood pressure and hypertension. Medical professionals argue that limiting intake of salty foods significantly reduces an individual's risk of heart disease, heart failure, and kidney disease.

Suggested Reading

Kurlansky, *Salt*.
Mintz, *Sweetness and Power*.

Questions

1. How did sugar travel around the world and become such a commodity?

2. Why was salt an important additive, and how is it linked to world history?

LECTURE
13

A BRIEF HISTORY
OF BREAD

Many food historians have argued that bread, in one form or another, has been a staple food of our species since we turned to the domestication of grains. Bread, in all of its forms, is one of the most widely consumed foods in the world. It's considered to be one of the hallmarks of cultivation and has been a key component of human diet for thousands of years. Bread knows no cultural bounds. Bread was also used as currency—and as a way to bribe the working class in ancient Rome. It is also tethered to the French Revolution and the civil rights movement in the United States.

The Making of Bread

- While no one knows exactly when humans began making bread, some recent studies suggest that bread making was happening around 30,000 years ago. The first bread may have been a paste that was made from gruel (water mixed with wild grains) and then heated. These early unleavened breads, or flatbreads, were compact, portable, and an important source of carbohydrates.

- The basic ingredients that form bread, grains and water that made gruel, were being consumed at least 22,500 years ago in the area that is now Iraq, Afghanistan, Turkey, Syria, and Israel.

- Humans cannot eat raw grains because our teeth and digestive systems can't handle it, so it must be cooked or fermented. Barley and wheat found imbedded in a grindstone by the Sea of Galilee have been dated to around 22,500 years old. The same site had a grouping of burned stones that archaeologists believe may have been used for cooking or baking.

- The earliest-known evidence of the use of a pestle and mortar was found in the south of France around 10,000 years ago to grind pigments. To make flour for bread, the grain must be ground, and to do this, ancient people undoubtedly first used a pestle and mortar. Because it was ground by hand by one person, it was not fine enough to be flour and was used to make gruel.

- The natural advancement was to use a larger mortar with 2 or more people alternately grinding the grain with a long-handled pestle. But to achieve finely ground flour, a device called saddle stones had to be invented. For this method, a top stone (pestle) is rubbed against a bottom stone (mortar) so that the grain is sheared.

- Not only does bread date to prehistoric times, but it's consumed all around the world and across cultures, with only a few exceptions. It was a small step for prehistoric people to turn their liquid gruel into a solid substance by frying it on hot stones. Campfires can also be used for baking bread.

- Historically, bread was much more than just something to eat; it was the economic and nutritional foundation for civilizations that formed in the Fertile Crescent and along the Mediterranean.

- Bread was a staple of ancient Mesopotamian and Egyptian cultures, as well as ancient Greek and Roman civilizations. It continued to feed most of Europe into the 19th century, and the wheat grown and harvested in the United States, Canada, and Australia is still a substantial part of those countries' economies.

- The next big step for bread was leavening—the key to making bread rise. We don't know when or how the first leavened bread came about, but we do know that ancient Egyptian hieroglyphs show bakehouses with dough rising next to bake ovens. Gradually, the production of leavened bread, light and airier than flatbread, became a routine.

- One Egyptian tomb painting depicting the bakery of King Ramses III shows the process of making bread: first trampling the dough, then tossing the dough by hand with water added, then placing molded dough in heated pans with large tongs, and last turning the dough with a shovellike utensil.

- The saddle-stones method is pictured in Egyptian paintings and Assyrian reliefs. Examples of the actual stones have been found in the Balkans and elsewhere.

- The Mesopotamians were using the saddle-stones method around 800 B.C., continually rotating the stones with draft animals or slaves. This milling process is the origin of how we make flour today. It produced a fine, white flour that quickly became a status symbol. The desire for the whitest flour continued into the modern era.

Bread and Religion

- Bread was such an important part of the Jewish religion that, centuries ago, it was sometimes referred to as food in general. Unleavened bread was even given as offerings to God at temple. Bread was not only important historically, but its significance can still be found in Jewish prayer: The blessing for bread is at the top of the hierarchy of food blessings, and full grace after a meal is not required unless bread has been served.

- For Christians, bread is equally vital. It symbolizes the living Jesus in their lives, as well as the need for divine nourishment. All 4 gospels in the Bible tell of Jesus feeding the masses with only a few loaves of bread and fish. And with the sacrament of the Eucharist, or communion, bread is seen as the body of Christ.

- Just as in the Jewish faith of old, bread in Islam refers to food in general. Because it is believed to be a gift from God, bread is protected, venerated, and never wasted. Destroying a place that produces food, including land and sea, is considered wasting

food and is strictly prohibited in Islam. Food is sacred in Islam because it sustains life, and life is sacred, so destroying a place that produces food is destroying life.

Bread and Controversy

- In the Assyrian empire, social order revolved around a centrally controlled bread ration. In Egypt, workers were paid with bread and grain, and soldiers could eat as much bread as they wanted.

- Rome, too, relied on a vast chain of bakeries and bread distribution centers. In the Middle Ages in Europe, bread was central to culture, religion, and survival.

- Bread was also used to keep the plebians, or Rome's working class, happy. They were the people who worked to keep the city going—farmers, craftsmen, bakers, and builders—and there were a lot of them. Emperor Augustus gave them free grain and free entertainment, ensuring that they would not starve and would not be bored and look to revolt.

- Even into the 1600s and beyond, bread remained an integral part of European diet. It was one of the cheapest forms of energy. Governments that were perceived as remiss about the supply of bread faced bread riots or worse.

- For centuries, bakers were the target of close regulation, and because of their control over people's sustenance, they were suspect. Bakers were accused of weight tampering, racketeering, and grain hording.

- Typically, the French rulers kept grain prices stable through regulation, but in the few years before the French Revolution in 1789, France experienced poor crops and poor harvests. As a consequence, the supply of grain was low for a country where bread was a food staple and energy source.

- When the supply diminished, the price of grain rose drastically. For the poor and working-class citizens, the price of grain was exorbitant. Because bread was the bulk of a peasant's diet, it meant that they starved.

- Bread was typically made with wheat, rye, and buckwheat at this time. To make the flour go further, bakers added "fillers": sawdust, dirt, hay, and even dung. Only France's upper class could afford white bread because wheat was very costly and underwent considerable refinement to make the best and whitest bread.

- With such a heavy reliance on bread, both the country peasants and city dwellers kept a close eye on grain prices. When grain prices went too high, bread riots broke out.

- Just prior to the French Revolution, bread riots became more and more common as the price of grain kept rising and some people were suspected of hoarding grain. In the early stages of the French Revolution, the aristocracy worried about the rising cost of bread and associated insurrections.

- But inflation and grain shortages continued to be a problem. With little access to bread, the riots grew and helped propel the revolution forward.

Advances in Bread Making

- Advances in milling grain came with power sources other than humans and animals. Waterpower made flour available to small communities and spread throughout western Europe. Wind-powered milling didn't come along until A.D. 1000, and then steam engine mills also made considerable advances.

- But none of these stone-mill techniques produced enough to supply cities. This all changed in the 1820s, when the efficient roller mill was tried in Hungary and quickly spread to other countries. The finer the grain is ground, the whiter it gets, and the roller mill achieved a white flour at a cheap cost, available to a large population.

- Unleavened bread, known as flatbread, was the beginning of bread for humans. Leavened, or rising, bread was a turning point for bread. The most common agent for leavening bread is yeast. The yeast eats the sugars present in grain and releases carbon dioxide, producing bubbles that make the bread lighter and airier.

- The ancient Egyptians were producing leavened bread long ago. But it wasn't until the invention of the microscope—and then, later, the famous experiments by Louis Pasteur—that the mystery of yeast was solved. In the late 1850s to early 1860s, Pasteur concluded, unequivocally, that yeast was a living organism and that active, living yeast cells cause fermentation.

- The most recent innovation and game changer for bread was mechanized slicing. For hundreds of years, bread was sold in whole loaves to be sliced by hand at home. Cookbooks and magazines from the 19th century even gave instructions for slicing bread.

- Then, in 1917, a jeweler named Otto Rohwedder invented the first mechanized bread slicer. Bread companies didn't believe that pre-sliced bread would be popular at first, so they held off on installing them in their factories for 11 years. But within 2 years after installation, 90% of store-bought bread was sliced by a machine.

- Industrial bread—bread that is produced in a factory—got its start in the 1840s and exploded in the 1890s and 1900s. These were times of widespread anxiety about germs, gender roles, and immigrants. In contrast, industrial white bread was perceived as a perfectly shaped, perfectly clean, perfectly white product.

- During World War II, bread-enrichment campaigns gave industrial bread another push and fueled people's desire to buy bread with plenty of added vitamins, believing it was healthier for them.

- From the Cold War to the early 1960s, industrial white bread was viewed as superior. In the early 1960s, it went global and played an essential role in America's postwar dominance of the world food system.

Bread as a Symbol

- Throughout history, the type of bread that a person ate defined his or her social status. The lightest and whitest bread was reserved for the elites. Dark, heavy bread was for everyone else. Even early 20th-century immigrants to the United States were looked down on if they ate dark, dense bread. White bread was thought to be distinctly American. But this changed in the 1960s, when bread consumption, in general, declined in the United States.

- The counterculture of the late 1960s, including antiwar activists and "back to the Earth" leaders, held up "plastic" white bread as a symbol of America's military smugness and cultural conformity. Food historians claim that white bread began to embody 2 very unfashionable things to the youth of America during this time: industrial origins and whiteness.

- The former ideal loaf of bread—white, fluffy and pre-sliced—had been so popular. It was America's favorite bread. But after the likening of white bread to mass culture and social discrimination was firmly engrained into the psyche of the American youth, they turned to other foods, and other breads. And when the nutritional benefits of whole wheat began being touted, it caused white bread's image to spiral even further downward.

- In the 1970s, industrial "health bread" became popular, riding on a wave of body-conscious consumers. The 1980s and 1990s saw the explosion of elite niche-market bread. In 2011, industrial-produced whole wheat bread became king. Today, organic, artisanal, multigrain breads are leading the industry.

Suggested Reading

Rubel, *Bread.*

Questions

1. When and where do scientists believe the first bread was made?

2. What is an example from history where bread played a central role in culture and/or religion?

THE SCIENCE
AND SECRETS
OF CHOCOLATE

Whether it comes in liquid or solid form, in bite size or jumbo size, as a bar, in a box, or atop a cone, the world loves chocolate. It comes in all shapes and sizes and is consumed all over the world. Chocolate has a rich history, spanning back thousands of years, that goes far beyond the culinary. In this lecture, you will learn about chocolate's trek around the world and explore not only its history and chemical properties but also its role in the current global market.

The History of Chocolate

- Chocolate comes from the cacao, or cocoa, tree, whose taxonomic classification is *Theobroma cacao*, a small evergreen tree found in tropical forested regions.

- The beans of the cacao tree have been used in Mesoamerica for centuries. A ceramic vessel found at an archaeological site in Veracruz, Mexico, dates some of the first residue of cacao beans to almost 4000 years ago.

- The cacao beans were not initially used for sweet treats but, rather, were initially harvested to make a somewhat bitter, frothy drink. Ancient Maya and Aztec beverages used fermented cacao seeds as the base of their drinks.

- The cacao tree, and its fruits, were important far beyond their role in cuisine. The Mayans worshipped a god of cacao, and the beans were thought to have been a powerful aphrodisiac. Chocolate was also thought to help with several ailments and was considered medicinal. Cacao beans were so valued, in fact, that they were used as currency.

- The first European to come into contact was Christopher Columbus, who did not recognize the beans that he encountered as anything special or valuable. Sometime between 1502 and 1504, during his fourth, and final, voyage to the New World, Columbus and his son Ferdinand seized a canoe in the Bay of Honduras.

- The canoe was filled with cocoa beans, which he was told were currency. Columbus is credited with bringing chocolate back to Europe, but when he did, they received much less attention than the spices, gold, and silver that he carried with him.

- When it did finally catch on, cocoa was a highly valued drink. This is also when it started becoming sweeter, as Spanish conquistadores are rumored to have been the first to add sugarcane to the drink.

- Chocolate historians claim that Spaniards kept chocolate a secret for the rest of Europe. The Godiva History of Chocolate states that cocoa did not show up in France until 1615, when it was introduced to the court of King Louis XIII when he married Anne of Austria. The first commercial chocolate shop was not opened until 1659.

- In 1657, chocolate is thought to have crossed the English Channel for the first time, but the European taste for chocolate really began in the 1700s.

- Unfortunately, hand in hand with this taste for the cacao bean also came the introduction of massive slave labor to produce and harvest it. Cacao was—and remains even today—harvested by hand all around the world. While some machinery can assist with part of the process, the main act of harvesting is very similar today as it was when cacao beans were first harvested.

- In the mid-1700s, wind-powered and horse-drawn mills were used to help speed up the production process, but it wasn't until the early to mid-1800s during the Industrial Revolution when mass production began.

Chocolate Companies

- One of the first chocolate companies was Cadbury, originally a British confectionary company founded in Birmingham, England, by John Cadbury in 1824. The company started manufacturing boxed chocolates by the late 1860s and is known as being the first company to put chocolate candy in a heart-shaped box for Valentine's Day.

- Between 1828 and 1829, a Dutch chemist named Coenraad van Houten created the first chocolate press. It was designed to remove the natural fat from chocolate, the so-called cocoa butter. This made it much cheaper, and much faster, to produce in large quantities.

- He also changed powdered chocolate by adding alkaline salts to the substance. This acted to give it a milder taste, changed the color to more of a red hue, and made it easier to mix better with water. This process is called Dutched chocolate, in honor of the nationality of its inventor. It's this cocoa that is used most frequently today—in hot cocoa, in ice cream, and for baking.

- After the invention of Dutching, which revolutionized the cocoa powder industry, the next major invention in the world of chocolate was in 1847. When cocoa went through van Houten's press, a dry cake of cocoa usually remained. This cocoa could then be pounded into powder and solidified. This process yielded the first chocolate candy bar, created by J. S. Fry & Sons, a British-based company.

- In 1875, a Swiss chocolatier named Daniel Peter was the first to invent milk chocolate—by adding powdered milk with chocolate liquor—which was very popular at the time. This powdered milk was produced by a baby food manufacturer named Henri Nestlé. The 2 men went on to found the Nestlé company, one of the world's leading food and beverage companies.

- In 1879, Rodolphe Lindt, a Swiss chocolatier and inventor, created the conching machine. This stirring machine allowed unpleasant aromas to evaporate off of the cocoa powder and gave the concoction a much finer consistency. He also revolutionized the chocolate industry by adding cocoa butter back into the mix. This paved the way for smooth and creamy chocolate to be produced on assembly lines.

- The most well-known American chocolate producers are Mars, Incorporated, and Hershey Company. Mars, Incorporated, was founded by Frank Mars, an American business magnate. In 1911, he started the Mars Candy Factory in Tacoma, Washington. In 1920, he moved his corporation to Minnesota and created the earliest incarnation of the company we know today—he called it Mar-O-Bar Company.

- In 1923, the company introduced the Milky Way chocolate bar. The Snickers bar followed in 1930, and in 1941, the company began producing M&Ms. Today, Mars produces more than 400 million candies every day all over the world.

- The Hershey Company, another great American chocolate manufacturer, was founded in Philadelphia by Milton S. Hershey in 1894. Before turning to chocolate, Hershey began making caramels. In 1907, Hershey introduced Hershey's chocolate kisses, and today roughly 80 million are produced each day.

The Dark Side of the Chocolate Industry

- Despite the fact that the Côte d'Ivoire, the so-called Ivory Coast of Africa, is the world's largest exporter of cocoa—producing almost a million and a half tons per year—the majority of the farmers who have been producing it, sometimes for their entire lives, have never tasted chocolate.

- While they grow and harvest the beans, they don't really know where their beans are going or what they are making. Furthermore, growers in West Africa often receive only about 3.5% to 6.4% of the final value of a chocolate bar—the chocolate bar that couldn't be produced without their beans.

- The controversy surrounding ways to empower cocoa farmers is a hot topic in sustainable business discussions today. Demand for chocolate is on the rise, and many consumer researchers are concerned that the demand will outstrip the supply.

- As the cost of living in West Africa rises, the farmers' inability to capture sufficient value from their cocoa crops means that they are increasingly turning to other means of survival.

- Because of this mass exodus from cocoa-bean production, the average age of a cocoa farmer in Côte d'Ivoire is 51 years old. This has led to a concern that when these farmers stop growing cocoa beans, the chocolate industry will take a massive hit.

- As a result, many companies are beginning to implement new policies to grow fair-trade chocolate. Fair-trade policies not only ensure that farmers growing cocoa enjoy safe and environmentally friendly working conditions, but that no slave labor or child laborers were used to produce the crop.

The Benefits of Eating Chocolate

- After decades of work, most people agree that there are benefits of eating chocolate. While the idea of eating chocolate for your health remains controversial, there is a lot of science behind the study of chocolate consumption.

- The sweet taste of chocolate coupled with its high-carbohydrate and fat content have made it a popular candidate food for cravings. Chocolate has always been touted as a food that has medicinal properties, ranging from claims that it is a stimulant, a relaxant, a euphoriant, a tonic, and even an antidepressant.

- There are several different types of chocolate, including cocoa powder, milk chocolate, white chocolate, and dark chocolate. Dark chocolate has a higher percentage of chocolate paste and a lower percentage of sugar when compared to either white or milk chocolate. Today, dark chocolate is often lauded as being good for your health.

- But chocolate's purported medicinal benefits are not new. They can be traced just about as far back as we can trace the use of the cacao bean itself. Aztec medical traditions included using the beans to soothe digestive complaints, control childhood diarrhea, reduce fevers, clear passages of blood in the stool, and as an expectorant for respiratory infections. It was also thought to promote strength and vigor.

- Later claims argued that chocolate had the power to increase breast milk production, assist with sleeping problems (both narcolepsy and insomnia), help to expel kidney stones, prevent syphilis, increase blood health, clean teeth, and even reduce the tendency for shyness.

- In the 21st century, research includes looking at the effect of chocolate on cholesterol concentrations and whether eating chocolate affects the release of phenethylamine, an organic compound known for psychoactive effects, or serotonin, which is thought to create feelings well-being and happiness.

- There is increasing attention being paid to polyphenols and flavonoids. Polyphenols are chemicals that are thought to have antioxidant properties. Flavonoids are a group of phytonutrients, or plant chemicals, that are found in most plant foods. They are argued to be powerful antioxidants and have anti-inflammatory and immune-boosting capabilities. They have even been shown to possess a range of cardiovascular protective properties, although this remains a bit controversial.

- Some studies have shown that flavonol-rich cocoa increases the appearance of healthy skin, can increase the amount of good bacteria in your gut, and may have neuroprotective effects— meaning that cocoa flavonols have an effect on the human brain.

- Chocolate is also known to be a stimulant. While it does contain modest amounts of caffeine, its major constituent is theobromine. While caffeine stimulates the nervous system, theobromine relaxes smooth muscle tissue and is a vasodilator, diuretic, and heart stimulant.

- Another often-touted power of chocolate is that it acts as a powerful aphrodisiac. And it's rumored that the ancient Mayans used to drink a special ceremonial drink made of cacao for betrothals and weddings. The scientific studies that have looked for a link between increased sexual arousal and chocolate consumption have not found a causal link.

- What about the idea of chocolate addiction? Is there really such a thing as a chocoholic? It turns out that much of the pleasure that we get from consuming chocolate is likely linked to the fact that the simple sugars it contains increase the serotonin in our blood. This is then linked to an improved mood. The so-called chocolate craving appears to be linked to psychological factors and is not really rooted in any addictive substances in cocoa or chocolate.

Suggested Reading

Cadbury, *Chocolate Wars*.
Coe, Coe, and Huxtable, *The True History of Chocolate*.
King, *Tea, Coffee, & Chocolate*.

Questions

1. What is the first evidence of chocolate consumption, and where did it occur?

2. What is the dark side of chocolate production, and how is the global chocolate industry trying to address concerns about production?

LECTURE
15

WATER: THE LIQUID OF LIFE

Water is everywhere—on Earth, on Mars, and all over the solar system. It's in our brains. It regulates the temperature of our bodies and of the planet. It's necessary to sustain life, and it can end life. But given how central it is to our daily lives, we know surprisingly little about it—where it came from, how much we really need, and who controls access to it with an increasingly growing global population.

Water on Earth

- Scientists still consider water's arrival on planet Earth to be somewhat of a mystery. For the last several decades, scientists have gone back and forth between thinking that it might be asteroids or comets that brought this substance to Earth.

- Both asteroids and comets contain ice, and the thinking is that when they collided with Earth, they may have contained oceans worth of the liquid. Some have suggested that asteroids and the comets from the Jupiter-Saturn region were the first water deliverers, when Earth was half the size it is today.

- Interestingly, this idea that water came after Earth was formed is not the only perspective on water's origins. Scientists from Woods Hole Oceanographic Institution believe that the water we have on our planet today is quite old and likely comes from the oldest meteorites.

- About 326 million cubic miles of water covers the Earth. But of all of the water on Earth, only a fraction of it is drinkable. Some estimates suggest that only 0.3% of Earth's water is available for consumption, and most of this is from groundwater aquifers, lakes, and rivers.

- In the United States, we use about 346 billion gallons of freshwater a day. Of this water, about 400 gallons per day are used for an average American family of 4. About 70% of that water is used indoors.

Drinking Water

- Nutritionists at Mayo Clinic say that if you're feeling thirsty, you might already be slightly dehydrated. They recommend drinking a glass of water with every meal—and when thirsty.

- Water regulates our body temperature, helps us digest our food and transport nutrients to our bodies, lubricates our joints and tissues, and can reduce the workload of our kidneys by flushing out waste products.

- Mayo Clinic recommends that every individual should drink between 2 and 3 liters of liquid per day—not necessarily only water—and advises that you may need to modify your water intake depending on whether you are pregnant, nursing, exercising, or suffer from a health condition.

- When you drink too much water, it inhibits your kidneys from effectively excreting the excess water. This means that the electrolyte content of your blood is now diluted, which can cause low sodium levels in your blood.

- Today, it seems like more and more people are carrying around water bottles to meet their minimum water requirements. Even though tap water is the second most consumed drink after carbonated soft drinks, bottled water is third.

- Bottled water is approximately 300 times more expensive than a gallon of tap water; some estimates even suggest that it might be as much as 2000 times more expensive. This is one reason that people are turning back to the tap for their water.

- In addition to the cost, there are other reasons that people are starting to ditch the plastic bottles. Contrary to what some people might think, bottled water is not necessarily more regulated or safer to drink than tap water, according to the Natural Resources Defense Council.

- And it's a tricky situation to figure out who regulates water. While the Food and Drug Administration regulates bottled water sold commercially, the Environmental Protection Agency regulates tap water.

- The majority of bottled water comes from springs and other natural sources, and about 25% comes from municipal sources, where the manufacturers essentially take tap water, treat it, purify it, and then bottle it and sell it at a greatly increased price.

- Most bottled water companies don't have to disclose on the labels where their water is sourced, which adds to much of the confusion for consumers. But some major producers are starting to label where they obtain their water.

- An additional deterrent to drinking bottled water is the plastic that the bottles are made from. Most bottled water comes in containers made out of polyethylene terephthalate, which some scientists have warned may yield endocrine disruptors, certain chemicals that can interfere with natural hormone production and function. The bottles may also leach poisonous metal if they are stored at high temperatures.

- In addition, drinking bottled water has negative consequences for environmental conservation. The average American drinks water from about 170 plastic bottles per year but only recycles about 40 of them.

- To quench our thirst for bottled water, we use about 17 million barrels of oil annually to produce the bottles that house the treated water. Plus, it takes about 2 liters of water to make every 1-liter bottle on the shelf of your supermarket or local convenience store.

- What can we do? The Environmental Protection Agency suggests drinking tap water. If you don't like the taste—or are worried about contaminants, depending on where you live—then try a filter. Additionally, there are many grassroots groups that are working to educate communities on water sustainability.

- Whether you choose to stick with plastic bottled water or filtered water, you're drinking water that is unfortified. Some dentists are now linking the increased consumption of unfluoridated filtered and bottled water with higher rates of tooth decay among children.

- Fluoride in drinking water remains a controversial issue. While the controlled addition of low levels of fluoride can reduce cavities, in high amounts fluoride can be dangerous. Chronic exposure can negatively impact bone formation, neurodevelopment, and kidney function. The World Health Organization's official position is in support of fluoride.

Freshwater Sources

- Water is a valuable resource—one that is necessary for survival. Yet according to a United Nations World Water Development Report in the early 2000s, only 3% of the world's water is drinkable. And 2.5% of this drinkable water is currently frozen and locked up in the Arctic and Antarctic. This means that the world must live on, and share, the approximately 0.5% of freshwater that is drinkable.

- The great majority of the freshwater available in the world is from aquifers. The United Nations has estimated that this amount is about equivalent to 4 trillion Olympic-sized swimming pools. The next-largest source is rainfall, providing about 47 billion Olympic swimming pools worth of water. Next come natural lakes, which yield about 36 billion Olympic swimming pools, followed by rivers and reservoirs (typically human-made), adding up to a paltry 3 billion Olympic-sized swimming pools worth of fresh, drinkable water.

- In the United States, we have several principal aquifers, many of which are made out of different rock types, from sandstone to igneous to carbonate rock. One of the largest is called the Ogallala Aquifer. It is one of the country's most important sources of water for drinking, industry, and crop irrigation.

- The Ogallala, filled with water that has been there for an estimated 3 million years, is disappearing. In some places, it is already gone. And there is no sign of recovery. Scientists say that if the Ogallala is drained, it would likely take more than 6000 years to fill up again naturally.

- This is bad news for the farmers in the grain belt, who not only need to make a living to feed their families but are responsible for growing the food that feeds our country.

- There is a small but growing trend for farmers to move away from total groundwater reliance. And some are using low- or no-till farming techniques, which means that the soil disturbance is kept to a minimum. This keeps the topsoil in place and increases the water-holding capacity of the soil.

- New irrigation techniques are also being developed, and new strains of drought-tolerant crops are being created. All of this can help, but it takes time. And it might not be enough.

- As new methods of water conservation are developed, populations are simultaneously expanding throughout the Great Plains regions serviced by Ogallala water. In addition, biofuels are now being used to grow some crops, and this method of farming requires an even greater amount of groundwater.

- Many farmers are turning to so-called dry or dryland farming—growing crops that do not rely on groundwater—as a way to avoid what they see as an eventuality of the Ogallala drying up. While dryland farming might save money on irrigation, and water, it means that the farmers take an economic hit. Production costs remain the same, but yields can drop to as much as 50%.

- But there is a glimmer of hope. A project funded by the Environmental Defense Fund encourages farmers to engage in native grassland restoration on their fields that no longer have any access to groundwater.

- By returning the land to grasslands, which used to house buffalo and pronghorn antelope, farmers are not only providing wildlife habitat, but might also be able to generate a different type of income—for example, through hunting or ecotourism.

- Despite the changes that are being made, all environmentalist experts agree that there is a water shortage. Even if it doesn't seem like it in the United States, water is a limited resource.

- The majority of the world's water is used for agriculture, which accounts for about 70% of freshwater extraction, and with a booming global population, water demands are expected to increase almost exponentially.

- As the world is shifting to a diet that is more heavily based on animal products, there are consequences for water. Meat and dairy products require more water to produce than a largely starch-based diet.

Water Consumption and Access

- Beyond the basic water consumption for thirst and the water for production of crops and industry, there is also something called virtual water consumption. Wealthier nations in the

Tips for Water Conservation

We can all make small changes in our daily lives that add up to big conservation. Some tips for water conservation include:

- turning the water off when you lather your face or brush your teeth,
- washing your dishes in a tub or sink of water rather than open-faucet washing,
- reducing the length of your showers, even by 1 minute,
- saving water that you might throw down the drain and using it for watering a plant or cleaning,
- fixing your household leaks,
- washing your car at a car wash that uses reclaimed water rather than your backyard hose,
- choosing low-flow water-efficient fixtures for your home,
- planting drought-resistant plants in your yard,
- shrinking or getting rid of your lawn,
- capturing rainwater,
- and drinking tap water or home-filtered water instead of bottled water.

postindustrialized West, such as the United States and countries in Europe, are not only maintaining or increasing their consumption of water, but are also now exporting their water footprints to nations in the developing world.

- A virtual-water footprint is the amount of water that is required to create the goods and services that we enjoy. Today, people in Europe and North America are consuming quite a lot of virtual water, as it's is embedded in all imported food and products. Virtual water also extends to almost everything that we use that comes from abroad. Many environmentalist groups now encourage people to think about their water footprint.

- Just like virtual water, wealthier nations consume more freshwater in general. Water is not evenly distributed around the world. More than half of the world's freshwater supply is controlled by fewer than 10 countries.

- After agriculture, industry is what requires the most amount of freshwater, and industrial use of water maps onto the wealth of a country. The highest-income countries use the greatest percentage of water for industry. These uses include energy production, product production, and wastewater disposal.

- The United States tops the chart, by far, for per-capita access to drinking water. Given the way that water is distributed around the globe, more than 1 billion people in the world do not have sustained access to clean drinking water. The majority of these people are living in Asia and sub-Saharan Africa.

- But while the pace of industrialization is increasing, industry is becoming more efficient. Agriculture is facing a similar situation. New technologies are being developed that will assist farmers all around the world to employ agricultural techniques that reduce reliance on groundwater. Awareness of water issues is increasing—all around the world and among all walks of life.

Suggested Reading

Feldman, *Water*.
Fishman, *The Big Thirst*.

Questions

1. How much water do medical professionals suggest that we drink on a daily basis?

2. What are the barriers to freely available drinking water for everyone all around the world?

LECTURE
16

BEER, MEAD, AND THE FUN OF FERMENTATION

From ancient Egypt and Mesopotamia to microbreweries in your neighborhood, people have always loved beer. In this lecture, you will discover our long history with fermentation: how, when, where, and why people began their love affair with fermented beverages—both beer, which is made from wheat, and mead, which is made from honey. Fermentation is the chemical breakdown of a substance by bacteria, yeasts, or other microorganisms. The process of fermentation that's involved in the making of beer, mead, wine, and liquor is one where sugars are converted to gases, acids, or alcohol.

Beer

- The discovery of beer was thought to have been accidental. It is argued to have taken place in Mesopotamia, one of the first great civilizations, sometime around 10,000 to 12,000 years ago. No one knows when the first beer was actually brewed. No traces of beer have been found prior to 10,000 years ago, but there is some tantalizing archaeological evidence of beer around 8000 years ago.

- While there are no written documents, we can estimate its origins from other lines of evidence. Ancient pictographs representing figures consuming beer have been found dating to around 4000 years ago in Mesopotamia, or modern-day Iraq.

- Grain crops flourished in the Near and Middle East region around the time of the advent of agriculture. Cereal grains, such as wheat and barley, were used for diet staples, which included beer and gruel.

- When our ancestors first began experimenting with cultivated grains, they made an important discovery: When gruel that had been made with malted grain was left out for a few days, it became fizzy and intoxicating—it became beer. While they didn't understand why this happened, they enjoyed it and believed it was a good thing.

- The accidental fermentation of fruit, making wine, and of water and honey, making mead, were likely discovered about the same time as beer. But fruit easily perished and honey was not always available, so beer became the most popular beverage. It was made from ingredients that were plentiful in the area and could be easily stored in animal skins, large shells, or even trees.

- Naturally, people started to experiment with different beer varieties. They noted, for example, that if you left your beer out for longer periods of time, it would ferment more. If you used malted grain, you got stronger beer. And if you used the same brewing vessel over and over again, you got better results. They also discovered that adding fruit, honey, and spices changed the taste.

- Early Mesopotamian records list more than 20 different types of popular beer. In both Mesopotamia and Egypt, beer was a big part of every aspect of human life, and it became their staple drink. It was an important part of their culture, religion, and social lives. All ages and social classes consumed beer, even children.

- The most evidence of ancient beer brewing is found in Egypt during the predynastic era, from around 7000 to 5000 years ago. Beer sediments have been found in jars at several locations in Egypt. Written text has also been uncovered from the Early Dynastic period (around 5000 years ago) recording that beer was a significant product at that time.

- The recipe for ancient beer was as follows: You needed water, grain, something to crush the grain, fire, a mixing vessel, and containers to collect the end product.

- Beer was consumed daily in ancient Egypt, often as a replacement for water. Because beer was made with boiled water, it became a more reliable means of liquid nourishment. And because it was boiled, it was safer to drink than water from a contaminated source. Although they didn't know it at the time, beer may have helped reduce illnesses.

- To Neolithic drinkers, alcoholic beverages such as beer and mead—with their intoxicating, mind-altering effects—seemed magical. The mysterious way that gruel changed into beer was also miraculous, so they thought that these drinks must be gifts from the gods. Many beer-drinking cultures made beer part of their religious proceedings.

- Beer may have been discovered in several different parts of the world simultaneously. Wheat and barley were also available to early civilizations in Europe. Chemical traces found in clay vessels throughout Europe, dating to around 5000 years ago, have been discovered in archaeological digs.

- The type of alcoholic beverages that a culture typically drinks are often dependent on what ingredients are available in a given region. Historically, in the case of Europe, southern Europeans were typically wine drinkers because grapes grew very well there, and northern Europeans were beer drinkers because barley, not grapes, grew well there

- Interestingly, there seems to have been a slight prejudice against beer in the Greek and Roman cultures. In ancient Greece, some texts indicate that beer was thought to be a drink consumed only by foreigners. Wine was thought to be a pure drink, while beer was tainted by yeast. Beer, despite the prejudice it may have suffered from in ancient Greece and Rome, rose to popularity after the fall of the Roman Empire.

- Several seaborne empires were established on the shores of the North Sea based on powerful navies and international trade: first the Vikings, followed by the German Hansa, the Dutch, and the Britons. For all 4, beer was a health requirement for sea voyages and became a trade commodity that brought them great wealth.

- Beer brewing was also taken up by monasteries in Europe. Monasteries first documented the use of hops in brewing, but hops were not used in earnest until around 1000 years ago. Hops are flowers of the hop plant that act to flavor the beer, stabilize the beer foam, and preserve the beverage.

- Other areas in Europe are also associated with beer brewing. During the Middle Ages, Vikings were also known as beer brewers.

- Medieval brewers not only mastered the technology of brewing beer but also developed brands and markets. This can be traced back to the times of Charlemagne, or Charles the Great, who ruled much of western Europe from around 768 to 814.

- In the 16th and 17th centuries, the Dutch commanded the largest fleet on the seas and established a trading empire stretching from New York to Jakarta. The rise of the Netherlands to this height was accompanied by the formation of a brewing industry unmatched in its time.

- The Britons established the next great fleet and made sure that they had plenty of nourishing and stable beer. For sea voyages, beer was indispensable for the sailors' health.

- By the beginning of the 18th century, a number of powerful commercial breweries had already been concentrated in the London area. By the end of that century, commercial large-scale brewing had been firmly established across all of Britain. During this time, tremendous changes in the beer industry were taking place.

- The industrialization of brewing started in the urban centers, where a mass market existed and new patterns in distribution emerged. Beer production varied depending on geographic region.

- With the widespread use of hops over the last 1000 years, given its natural preservation properties, beer began to be transported around the world. As hops migrated around the world, they adapted to different climates and soils. When this happened, the beer's taste varied depending on the geographic location.

- The giant leap in brewing during the 18th and 19th centuries was, for the most part, the result of scientific principles put in place. The process of fermentation still remained a mystery in the early 1800s; it wasn't until 1838 when 3 scientists independently discovered that yeasts are living organisms. Between 1855 and 1875, Louis Pasteur brought to light the role of yeast in alcoholic fermentation and the physiological nature of fermentation.

- At the turn of the 20th century, beer production and consumption had spread all over the world. Europe still led the way in beer production, with a 79% share. Today, they make only about 34% of the world's beer, as the Americas and Asia step up their own production and beer markets.

Mead

- Mead, which nearly died out after the Middle Ages, is currently the fastest-growing segment of the U.S. alcohol industry. Like beer, mead can be traced back to at least 800 years ago. Also like beer, it was discovered accidentally. Some believe that it was first consumed by our foraging ancestors, who stumbled on the drink when honey and water were fermented.

- These are the sources that claim that mead is the oldest alcoholic beverage, even older than beer. Because domesticated grains (to make beer) didn't come along until ancient people settled down to farm, around 10,000 years ago, it stands to reason that honey-based mead could have come first.

- Honey hunting by nomadic people was already well established by 10,000 years ago, and all you need to make mead is honey, water, and wild yeast. Both honey and mead played an important role in the daily lives of ancient people and those that followed, weaving a thread through their mythologies and rituals.

- The production of mead has been found through many sources of ancient history all over the world. Chemical analyses of ancient organics absorbed into pottery jars from an early Neolithic village in China revealed a mixed fermented beverage of rice, honey, and fruit dating to around 8000 years ago. In Europe, sample mead ingredients have been found in the ceramics of the Bell-Beaker culture of Bronze Age Europe, around 3500 years ago.

- Fermentation requires sugar. Raw materials for sugar sources, such as wild berries, fruits, and tree sap, were widely available to pre-Neolithic peoples, but not year-round. And storing them was equally difficult.

- Even in a pre-farming era, these sugar sources would have been available year-round only in warm climates, not temperate ones, such as most of Europe. The only exception is honey. So, we can presume that, in Europe, honey was the basis for the first fermented drink, mead.

- By the 7th century in England, every castle had a mead hall, where mead was served to guests with great ceremony. About 1000 years later, mead was still being served in England.

- Alcoholic drinks made from honey were common among the people of Scandinavia, Gaul, Europe, and Greece. In the Middle Ages, particularly in northern countries where grapevines do not flourish, mead was a favored beverage. Mention of mead can be found in Celtic and Anglo-Saxon literature. Mead has also enjoyed consistent time in the limelight of both Gaelic poetry and Irish folklore and spans back historically to the ancient Greeks, who referred to it as ambrosia.

- Many Norse legends tell of gods and goddess drinking mead to enhance their powers and help them relax. Besides its intoxicating influence on drinkers, mead was also thought to have great medicinal value.

- Later, taxation and regulations governing the ingredients of alcoholic beverages led to commercial mead becoming a more obscure beverage. Some monasteries kept up the old traditions of mead making as a by-product of beekeeping, especially in areas where grapes could not be grown.

- Today, mead is making a comeback. Like beer and wine, mead can be made in a number of varieties: light, heavy, sweet or dry, still or sparkling. Ingredients such as fruit juices, fruits, spices, herbs, hops, and grains are often added to give it more flavor and diversity. You can even find mead on the menus of quite a few microbreweries.

Suggested Reading

Alba-Lois and Segal-Kischinevzky, "Yeast Fermentation and the Making of Beer and Wine."

Bostwick, The Brewer's Tale.

Braun, *Buzz.*
Standage, *A History of the World in 6 Glasses.*

Questions

1. What did poet John Ciardi mean when he stated, "Fermentation and civilization are inseparable"?

2. What has led to the recent increase in local, regional craft breweries across the United States?

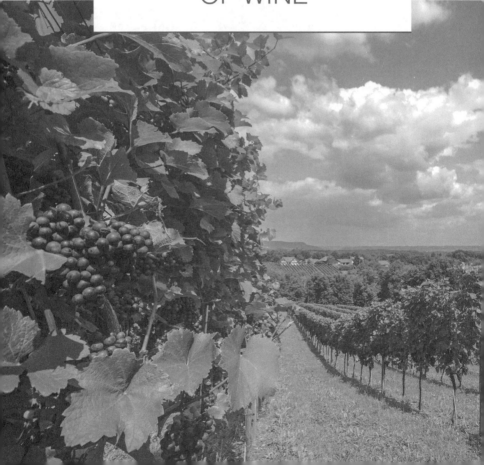

LECTURE
17

HUMANITY'S LOVE
OF WINE

From ancient Egyptian pharaohs, to Greek philosophers, to contemporary foodies—across time and space—people have always had a love affair with wine. This lecture will explore this love affair by examining the history of wine, the way it's made, and what precisely goes into your glass.

The History of Wine

- Wine grapes are grown on every continent in the world, except Antarctica. Interestingly, however, grapes from a single Eurasian species, *Vitis vinifera*, make up about 99% of the world's current wine. Wine experts marvel at the fact that an almost infinite variety of tastes, acidities, and aromas can emerge from this one species.

- Detailed descriptions of the invention of wine in ancient texts are somewhat hard to come by. Pliny the Elder devoted an entire chapter to the subject in his tome, *Natural History*, which was written between A.D. 77 and 79 and was one of the first classical manuscripts to be printed, in 1469.

- Archaeology—together with archaeobotany, the study of ancient plants—provides the best clues to uncovering when and where the first wine showed up. One of the oldest-known wineries was found in what is present-day Armenia, dating to more than 6000 years ago. Evidence for wine outside of a winery context has been found dating to around 7000 years ago in Iran.

- In his book *Uncorking the Past: The Quest for Wine, Beer, and Other Alcoholic Beverages*, Patrick McGovern, one of the world's foremost experts on ancient wine, argues that biomolecular evidence of wine (in the form of residue) has been found all over the world. He argues that several studies suggest that the mountains of Armenia, Georgia, and neighboring countries are the likely birthplace of wine making, or viticulture, the science and production of grapes specifically for making wine.

- One of the oldest types of white wine is called retsina, which is associated with Greek culture. These types of wine date as far back as 2000 years ago and are made with tree resin. It is thought that the tree resin, often pine, was used long before the invention of impermeable glass bottles. The pine not only infused the wine with flavor but also helped to keep unwanted oxygen out of the containers that might spoil the wine when it was stored for extended periods of time.

- There is evidence outside of Greece for white wine even earlier in history. The famous King Tutankhamun, or King Tut, of ancient Egypt died more than 3300 years ago. A team of archaeologists analyzed the residue in the tall double-handled jars found inside his tomb and discovered evidence of white wine, which was surprising because wine had historically been considered to be almost exclusively red in ancient Egypt.

- Red wine dates to around 7000 or 8000 years ago, and white wine is a bit younger by a few thousand years. But McGovern thinks it's possible that wine dates to even before we have archaeological evidence for it. In one of the chapters in his book, he theorizes that our ancestors, possibly early members of the genus *Homo*, stumbled upon the fermentation process while collecting and storing wild berries and other small fruits.

- The argument is that when our ancestors stored these berries in a container, or even a hollowed-out space, for short periods of time, they would start the fermentation process. The foragers, upon consuming the fermented fruit, may have noticed the funny feelings that they had after eating the sweet and intoxicating food.

- Another iteration of this hypothesis is that certain wild grape species might have fermented right on the vine. The fruits are particularly vulnerable to mold, which can concentrate the sugar content, and once the skin is broken, the grape is now particularly vulnerable to fermentation—due to the wild yeasts living on the exterior.

- McGovern argues that our forebears were quite clever, and very observant, and that eventually they would have noticed the strange behavior of the birds and other animals who ate the fermented fruits. This may have prompted them to carry out some rudimentary fermentation experiments of their own.

From Vine to Wine

- While there are many different varietals and the process varies from region to region, the basic steps for making wine are as follows.

   1. The first step is picking the grapes. Interestingly, white wine can be made from either white or red grapes. Grapes can be harvested during the day or night, depending on the climate and the harvest. The grapes can either be collected by hand, plucked from the vine, or removed by a machine.

   2. The next step, regardless of when or how the grapes were picked, is crushing. A machine called a crusher/destemmer is used almost exclusively for the job. This machine destems and then lightly crushes the grapes.

      a. For white wine, the grapes are then moved into a press, where the skins are removed and the sweet juice is collected and transferred into tanks. Once the juice has settled, it is racked, meaning that the sedimentation is filtered out and the juice is transferred to another tank. The key is to get a clear, frothy juice, which can range in flavor, depending on the grape, from sweet to sour.

b. While grapes for red wine are also destemmed and crushed, they are then moved directly into a vat to start the fermentation process. The grapes keep their skins on, which is what gives red wine its color.

3. The next step in the process is fermentation, in which yeasts convert sugars into alcohol. White wines are usually fermented at much cooler temperatures than red wines, which acts to preserve the fruity flavors. For both red and white varietals, yeast is added to the vats at this stage. To increase the fermentation, some vintners add specific nutrients to speed along the process and bolster the fermentation.

4. Once the fermentation process is complete, red wines get racked. Once they clarify the wine, it then gets aged in barrels. Wine makers can choose to age their wine for several months or several years. They can choose to do it in stainless-steel containers or oak. They can do it in regular barrels or "toasted" containers that have been charred. Oak barrels are often used with red wines, while steel tanks are more routinely used for zesty and crisp white wines.

5. The next stage is bottling the wine. White wines are typically filtered again before bottling, and they often age for much less time than red wines. Many white wines are ready to bottle after a few short months, whereas most dry reds can take up to 2 years before they're ready to go into the bottle.

6. Once they are bottled, they are finished off with either a cork or a screw top—a battle that has been going on for decades. Many wine makers argue that a screw cap is better for white wines or red wines that are meant to be consumed young. The screw top keeps the bottle better sealed, making sure that no oxygen enters. More complex wines, such as Chardonnays or big reds, such as Cabernets and Merlots, can benefit from a little oxygen in the bottle, which a cork allows.

Varietals

- The art of wine appreciation is a difficult skill to master. Even the number of different types of wines is difficult to pin down; most estimates put it around 200.

- The basic distinction between white and red has to do with the way in which the wine is fermented and/or aged. But beyond that, how many different varietals are there?

  - Your basic red can be further divided into sweet, herbal dry, or fruity dry—not to mention rosé, which is created when the grapes are left in contact with skin for only a short period of time.

  - Dessert wines are typically sweet but usually only imbibed with dessert. Some sommeliers suggest that a sweet fortified white wine should be drunk before a meal, whereas a sweet fortified red wine, such as a port, should be drunk after a meal.

  - You can also have dry whites and sweet whites.

  - Sparkling wines can be red, white, or rosé varietals.

- For beginners, most wine enthusiasts argue that you must know the following 8 types:

  - Whites: Riesling, Pinot Gris or Pinot Grigio, Sauvignon Blanc, and Chardonnay.

  - Reds: Pinot Noir, Zinfandel, Syrah, and Cabernet Sauvignon.

  - There are more than 1000 different types of grapes that get used to make hundreds of different wines.

Sulfites and Tannins

- Beyond grapes, other things that might be in your wine are sulfites and tannins—hot topics among wine drinkers.

- The term "sulfite" refers to sulfur dioxide, a preservative that is used widely throughout the food and beverage industry to prevent browning and discoloration. Sulfites can be found in a wide range of processed foods, ranging from tuna to cheese and wine. Wine is one of the only foods that lists on the label that it contains sulfites, so this has led to mass confusion by consumers.

- There is a popular myth that sulfites are bad for our health and that consuming them can lead to headaches. The data suggests, however, that most people can tolerate sulfites. Studies have shown that some people can be very sensitive to sulfites—around 1 in 100. It is most common among asthmatics.

- Sulfites also occur naturally, meaning that about 99% of all wines sold contain sulfites. Some organic wines do not add sulfites, and they say as much on the label. But for those with a sulfite sensitivity, even organic wines might lead to negative reactions.

- Tannins are organic substances found in plant material. They are present in grape skins, seeds, and stems—so, naturally, they got into wine. Tannins are naturally occurring polyphenols, which have been argued by many health enthusiasts to be beneficial.

- Polyphenols have been said to reduce the risk of cardiovascular disease, neurodegenerative diseases, and even diabetes. To get these tannins, however, you need to drink tannic wines, or wines that have a high tannin content.

- *The American Journal of Clinical Nutrition* states that red wine can contain 10 times the tannin content of white wine, because white wines have all of the grape skins removed during processing.

- Many people blame the headaches they have the morning after they have consumed wine on a high tannin content. The jury is still out on whether this is the likely culprit. Most research suggests that it might, at least most of the time, be linked with dehydration, the sugar content of wine, or the histamines that are present in aged, dry red wines.

Suggested Reading

McGovern, *Uncorking the Past*.
Standage, *A History of the World in 6 Glasses*.

Questions

1. How old is the practice of wine making, or viticulture, according to historians and archaeologists?

2. What is malvidin, and how does it influence wine?

LECTURE
18

COFFEE: LOVE
OR ADDICTION?

Most people consume caffeine every day, throughout the day, without even thinking about the fact that it's a psychoactive drug. While other foods contain caffeine, the majority of it in the United States is imbibed—consumed in soft drinks, coffee, and tea. This lecture will track our love of—or addiction to—coffee throughout history and around the world.

The History and Global Market of Coffee

- A few different regions claim to be the true birthplace of coffee. Some of the earliest historical records indicate that the beginnings of coffee are linked to a trade relationship between what is present-day Yemen and Ethiopia.

- It is unclear what was happening in Ethiopia during this exact time, because no historical records exist, but in Yemen, Sufi monks kept records. These monasteries documented either the drinking of coffee or knowledge of the coffee bean from as far back as the 12th or 13th century. By the 16th century, coffee had traveled to the rest of the Middle East, Turkey, northern Africa, Europe, Indonesia, and the Americas.

- But coffee wasn't always thought of as liquid gold. In fact, it faced considerable resistance throughout the centuries and was banned in several countries throughout the world—in places such as in Mecca, Constantinople, the Ottoman Empire, Italy, and Prussia—at different times.

- Today, the global coffee market is booming. Coffee shops have a 7% annual growth rate. And no coffee shop is more well known the world over than Starbucks. It is America's coffee king—and the third-largest restaurant chain in the United States.

- Starbucks started in 1971 as a store that initially sold only beans and coffee-brewing equipment. It wasn't until 1986 when one of the owners, who had left the initial business, purchased the stores from his other original business partners and created the first iteration of the franchise we know today. After taking Seattle by storm, the company conquered America and then the global market.

- In addition to being a billion-dollar company, Starbucks is often associated with the fair-trade movement. In 2000, Starbucks agreed for the first time to carry fair-trade-certified whole-bean coffee. This shed a global light on the economics and environmental impacts of coffee production.

- While the coffee business is growing, the actual profits for coffee-producing countries have been declining precipitously for the last several decades. While the countries producing the coffee saw a 40% decrease in profit, consumers started paying a hiked-up price that increased by more than 30%.

- The fair-trade movement began in the late 1980s in the Netherlands and now includes a global market of fair-trade producing and purchasing relationships. Fair-trade certified means that farmers are guaranteed a fair minimum price. It also connects the farmers with importers, creating long-term and sustainable trade relationships.

- Fair-trade concerns are not the only issue giving coffee a dark side. According to the World Wildlife Fund, 37 out of the 50 top countries with the highest deforestation rates are coffee-producing countries.

- Coffee was originally grown in the shade, which can increase production output. In recent decades, there has been a move to shift planting into the sun. The new non-shade-growing techniques include pesticide use and massive deforestation—which allow greater output but are unsustainable.

- Not only are these techniques thought to reduce the flavor, but they also destroy the native habitat for flora and fauna indigenous to the areas. You can now buy shade-grown and bird-friendly coffee.

From Seed to Cup

- The National Coffee Association says that there are 10 steps coffee takes to get from seed to cup:

    1. The first step is planting. The seeds are typically planted in the shade during the rainy season to ensure that the soil remains moist while the seedlings are maturing. Depending on the type of coffee, it can take an average of about 4 years for the plant to mature. In the first 2 to 4 years, the plant will produce small white flowers, which only last a few days and are then replaced by green leaves and, shortly thereafter, berries, often called coffee cherries, as most species turn a dark red when they are ready to be harvested.

    2. The second step is harvesting. The timing of the berry picking is critical. There are 2 major types of harvesting: strip picked or selectively picked.

        a. In strip-picked coffee, all of the berries are stripped off of the branch at one time, either by hand or by machine.

        b. In selectively picked coffee, only the ripe berries are harvested, and they are done so by hand. This ensures that only the berries that are at their peak of ripeness are selected.

    3. The third step is processing the berries. Once the berries have been picked, it is time to process them, and this must happen quickly, before the fruits spoil. Each berry has 2 cavities, or locules, which house the beans. There are 2 methods

of processing the coffee cherries: the wet method and the dry method.

a. The wet method entails removing the pulp from the berry so that the bean inside is dried with only a thin skin surrounding it. The beans first go through a pulping machine that separates the skin and pulp of the berry from the bean. Then, the beans are separated by weight; the heavier beans are the ripe ones. The beans are then transported to fermentation tanks filled with water. They will sit in these tanks for up to 2 days, as the outer layer of parchment is slowly removed from the bean. Once they are rinsed, they are dried.

b. The dry method of processing the coffee cherries is the old method, and one that is still used in many parts of the world today. It is a common practice in geographic regions that might have limited access to large amounts of water. In this method, the newly picked berries are simply laid out in the sun to dry. They are turned frequently, to deter spoilage, and then covered at night to protect them from any rainfall. This process is variable but can last up to several weeks.

4. The fourth step is drying the beans. If the beans were processed by the wet method, this is the stage in the process where those beans are dried. They are either dried by the sun, spread on the tops of tables or on the floor, and turned regularly, or they are machine dried in large industrial tumblers.

5. The fifth step is milling the beans. Now that the beans have been dried, they have to be cleaned. Hulling, which is done by a hulling machine, is when the entire dried husk is removed from the berry. Polishing, which is also done mechanically, is another optional step where any skin that might remain on the bean is removed after hulling. The second part of the milling process involves sorting the beans by size. Only the highest-quality beans are then readied for export.

6. The sixth step is export. Dried, hulled, and cleaned beans are placed into jute or sisal bags and loaded onto ships to be distributed around the world. The National Coffee Association estimates that around 153 million bags, each weighing around 60 kilograms, are produced each year.

7. The seventh step is quality testing. The process of testing the coffee for quality is referred to as cupping. The taster, or the cupper, will first inspect the beans visually. The beans are then roasted in a small roaster on site, ground, and prepared for consumption. The cupper will smell the coffee, inhaling its aroma. After letting the coffee rest, the cupper will smell it again before taking a spoonful of the brew.

8. The eighth step is roasting the beans. Roasting is what turns the green coffee beans into the dark-brown coffee beans that most people are familiar with. Mechanical roasters rotate the beans throughout the process to keep them from being burned. Once they reach a temperature of about 400° internally, they start to turn brown and the fragrant oil emerges. This is the quintessential coffee aroma. There are several different types of roast, including the American, French, European, and Viennese roasts. Once the beans are roasted, they are cooled (using either water or air) and then packaged for consumption.

9. The ninth step is grinding the beans. Once you have whole, roasted coffee beans, they need to be ground to brew your cup of coffee. There are different types of coarseness, depending on how you drink your coffee: coarse grind, used for French press, vacuum coffee makers, or percolaters; medium grind, used in drip coffee makers; fine grind, used in some drip makers and in stove-top espresso pots; superfine grind, used in most espresso machines; and super-superfine grind, used in Turkish coffee.

10. The tenth step is brewing your coffee. Depending on how you like to drink your coffee, the amount of time that your grounds will be in touch with hot water is up to you. A general rule of thumb, however, is that the finer the coffee grind, the more quickly it should be prepared and consumed.

Caffeine

- In addition to the delicious taste, rich aroma, and long culinary history of coffee, we also find the caffeine irresistible. According to the U.S. Food and Drug Administration (FDA), caffeine naturally occurs in more than 60 different plant species. But the majority of caffeine on the planet is consumed in coffee form.

- Caffeine is a stimulant. While making you feel more awake, which some see as a positive benefit of drinking caffeine, there are also negative side effects, including having the jitters, difficulty sleeping, increased heart rate, high blood pressure, nausea, headaches, and dehydration.

- But many people are willing to pay this price for increased alertness, which is thought to be the top reason people turn to caffeine. This alertness is due to the fact that caffeine is similar to a molecule called adenosine, which is found in human cells and plays an important role in biochemical processes.

- According to the FDA, after drinking caffeine, it reaches its peak level in your bloodstream within 1 hour. It can stay in your system for between 4 and 6 hours, which is why most people need an afternoon pick-me-up.

- The FDA suggests that 4 to 7 cups of coffee per day is likely too much. Their recommendation is 1 to 2 5-ounce cups of coffee each day. Mayo Clinic suggests that about 400 milligrams should be the daily limit.

- While much of the research on whether caffeine helps us be more productive, remains somewhat contentious, there does seem to be a general consensus that caffeine can, in some instances, increase work output.

- Some studies have also shown that caffeine may assist with some declarative or explicit memory tasks—information that is memorized, stored, and then retrieved. One study found that caffeine consumption had a tendency to energize people when they were working on repetitive tasks. And there is evidence that caffeine might have positive effects on staying the effects of Alzheimer's disease.

- Regular, moderate intake of caffeine has been found to prevent or slow memory decline in the elderly. Research on mouse models has shown that caffeine slows the growth of proteins that create plaque in the brain, one of the attributes of Alzheimer's. To enjoy these benefits, researchers have suggested that individuals with mild memory impairment should drink about 3 cups of coffee a day.

Suggested Reading

Braun, *Buzz*.
King, *Tea, Coffee, & Chocolate*.
Standage, *A History of the World in 6 Glasses*.
Wild, *Coffee*.

Questions

1. What evidence do scientists look to when determining if coffee is addictive?

2. What criteria have to be met for coffee to be categorized as fair-trade certified?

THE ROOTS OF TEA

Tea has mystical origins and a strong foothold in global history and is one of the most widely imbibed beverages in the world. The birthplace of tea is the East—most likely China. Its precise origins, however, are unclear. The story goes that Emperor Shen Nung, the second of China's legendary emperors who ruled in the 3rd millennium B.C., accidentally discovered tea when wind blew the leaves of a bush into the hot water that he was boiling. From that day to this, tea has taken the world by storm.

Tea in Asia

- Experts say that there may be as many as 1500 different types of tea. All types stem from an evergreen bush called *Camelia sinensis*. This plant species likely evolved in the Himalayas, near what is today the border between India and China. It remains unclear how tea initially traveled from this area to China, but the history books tell us that it was likely with the assistance of Buddhist monks more than 1000 years ago.

- Tea began as a medicinal and religious beverage and eventually became a domestic drink in China. It was originally harvested from wild-growing *Camelia* bushes, and when the drink began to gain popularity, it had to be grown and cultivated.

- Tea rose in popularity during the famed Tang dynasty in China, from the year A.D. 618 to 907. This time in history is regarded as a golden age of cosmopolitan life in China; it was the largest and wealthiest empire in the world.

- The beverage flourished, largely due to its antimicrobial or antiseptic properties. Not only do the tea leaves contain tannins,

which are thought to have antibacterial effects, but the water is also boiled before consumption.

- It is thought that drinking hot tea may have reduced the rates of typhoid, dysentery, and cholera during this time in China. In addition to these health effects, tea was also a great driver for the ancient Chinese economy.

- At a time when China was already enjoying successful trade relationships with India, Japan, and Korea, the tea industry was booming. China exported silk, tea, paper, and ceramics on the famed Silk Road overland trade routes as well as via sea routes. Tea was so valuable that it was used as currency in some parts of central Asia.

- Tea fell from grace for a short period of time during the 13th century when China was under Mongolian rule. Under Genghis Khan's rule, the national beverage of choice was that of the Mongols: the fermented milk of a mare, called kumis.

- Once the Mongols were expelled from China, tea drinking was a way to reassert Chinese culture. The celebration of tea became synonymous with the Ming dynasty, which lasted from 1368 to 1644.

- Up until this time, the most popular and most commonly produced type of tea in China was called block tea, and these bricks of finely ground post-oxidized tea, sometimes mixed with binding agents such as flour or manure, were used as currency.

- The founding emperor of the Ming dynasty, Zhu Yuanzhang, abolished the use of block tea, or so-called cake tea, in favor of loose-leaf tea. It is thought that the black tea and green tea that we drink today is from the Ming dynasty—minus the manure.

- The old way of drinking tea, from the bricks, was an elaborate process. First, a piece of the large brick had to be removed, cleaned, and then toasted. This piece was then pounded and ground into a powder. The final step was whisking it with hot water.

- This process was time consuming and required many tea utensils. Once people began drinking loose-leaf tea, it simplified the process immensely. This is when teapots became fashionable, and the teapot has been associated with the leaves ever since.

- In Japan, tea was first written about as early as the 9th century. The first tea was brought from China and was likely in brick form. The oldest tea specialty book in Japan is translated to *How to Stay Healthy by Drinking Tea* and was written by Myoan Eisai, a priest who had traveled to China to study religion.

- In the book, tea is called the elixir of life. And up until this book was introduced, around the year 1191, when Eisai was rumored to bring back tea seeds to Kyoto, the beverage was largely consumed by the elite class. Eisai was instrumental in introducing tea to the Japanese warrior class, or samurais.

- Eisai is thought to be the founder of Zen Buddhism and was the first to cultivate tea for strictly religious purposes. The Japanese tea ceremony was originally tethered to Zen Buddhism and became an integral part of the Japanese culture—and remains so today. Over centuries, the Japanese tea ceremony has changed.

- There are several different types of tea ceremonies, depending on the occasion, season, or even time of day. They all involve their own set of highly choreographed movements that must be learned by heart.

- Tea is so intricately linked with Japanese culture that green tea is now commonly referred to simply as Japanese tea. There are many different types of green-leaf varieties in Japan, including matcha, gyokuro, and sencha. Today, these teas have as much cultural significance as ever.

Tea in Europe

- Tea started being consumed in Europe around the 16th century, when Portuguese missionaries returned to Europe from China with the beverage in hand. Tea did not become a large-scale trade item until the Dutch entered into the tea business.

- The first shipments of tea from China and Japan entered Europe in 1610—brought in by the Dutch East India Company. Tea was also brought in over land, on the backs of camels, into Russia and then to cities such as Amsterdam and Paris.

- But tea, which is now associated with British culture, was originally introduced by a Portuguese queen. When Charles II's queen, Catherine of Braganza, moved from Portugal, she wanted to continue drinking tea, which she had grown up consuming.

- Her wish was granted in 1664, when Britain placed its first order for tea: 100 pounds of tea from China, shipped from Java, came into British ports and continued flowing into Britain. By 1685, 12,070 pounds were imported annually, and by 1750, the annual import reached about 4,700,000 pounds.

- The 18th century was a bit different. Tea was very expensive but was liked by everyone, not just the wealthy. To meet the demands of the less-affluent tea drinkers, a lot of tea was smuggled into the country illegally.

- The Commutation Act of 1784 reduced the tax on tea from 119% to 12.5%. This drastic decrease was meant to stimulate trade and revenue for the British East India Company.

- Before the Commutation Act, the East India Company had a surplus of tea due to the smuggling. The company asked the British Parliament for permission to export to the 13 British colonies in North America.

- The tea, which was quite popular with the colonists, was then taxed at $3 per pound. People were outraged by this controversial Tea Act of 1773. On December 16, 1773, a political protest by the Sons of Liberty in Boston, Massachusetts, involved sneaking aboard 3 East India Company ships in the harbor and throwing the tea overboard.

- The patriots of the movement are credited with the saying, "Taxation without representation is tyranny," which meant that they did not want to be taxed by a British Parliament in which they were not represented but wanted to be taxed by their own elected officials.

- The British Parliament was not pleased with the Tea Party protest and responded with the Coercive Acts in 1774. Among other things, this legislation ended self-government in Massachusetts.

Conflict then escalated, and the American Revolutionary War began in 1775.

- Interestingly, as a consequence of the Boston Tea Party, tea became less popular. In some circles, it was even unpatriotic to drink. But this label didn't last. Today, tea can be found in 80% of all American homes. In the United Kingdom, however, tea remains the top beverage consumed.

Types of Tea

- Pure tea, made from *Camellia sinensis*, includes green, black, white, pu-erh (meaning fermented), and oolong varieties.

- Herbal tea isn't actually considered tea by purists, as it is not made from plants of the *Camellia* genus. Herbal teas are made from the infusion of spices, herbs, and any other plant material in hot water and typically don't contain caffeine. Herbal teas were often considered to have medicinal properties in ancient Egyptian practices as well as traditional Chinese medicine.

- Herbal tea is typically consumed the same way as non-herbal teas. Any combination of dried flowers, seeds, leaves, and roots are steeped in hot water. After this point, the tea can be consumed either hot or cold. Some of the most popular herbal teas include peppermint, jasmine, ginger, ginkgo biloba, hibiscus, and chamomile.

- Of the true teas, black tea, which is referred to as red tea in China, is generally thought to be the strongest in terms of flavor. This has to do with the level of oxidation, which is greater than other types of tea. Oxidation is a set of chemical reactions that tea leaves go through that browns them and is responsible for the flavor and aroma.

- Oxidizing tea is a critical step in its production, as it greatly alters the flavor, look, and chemical composition of the tea leaf. In general, tea tends to get darker in hue as it oxidizes. Black teas are generally thought of as fully oxidized or partially oxidized. Oolong teas are considered to be partially oxidized. White and green teas are often considered to be unoxidized—but that isn't quite accurate. Some green teas are lightly oxidized.

- In addition to actual different types of teas—such as black, green, white, etc.—there are also different ways to imbibe the tea. Loose-leaf tea is probably the most common form of tea worldwide. It is argued by tea enthusiasts that this is the best way to consume your tea, as these leaves are argued to have more flavor, aroma, and antioxidants than their counterparts in the tea bag.

- In addition to the choice of whether to make your tea with loose-leaf tea or bagged tea, you also have the choice of drinking it hot or cold. Iced tea has been consumed in both the United Kingdom and the United States since the 1800s. Today, iced tea remains incredibly popular, and you can find many iterations of the drink.

- Different types of teas are also often thought to have different health benefits. There are many purported positive health benefits from drinking tea. Studies have shown that tea drinkers appear to be less likely to have livor disease, depression, coronary heart disease, or strokes.

- Green tea, in particular, has been shown in a few studies to slightly reduce the risk of prostate and endometrial cancer. Some studies also provide limited evidence that drinking green tea might help people lose weight.

- Tea contains polyphenols, and many of the health claims of tea are linked to its phenolic content—the phenols and polyphenols, plant components that contain natural antioxidants. The polyphenol concentration in any given tea is based on the type consumed, brew time, amount consumed, and temperature.

- While there is good scientific research to suggest that people who eat a diet high in antioxidant-rich fruits and vegetables have lower risks of several diseases, it remains unclear whether this is directly related to the antioxidants or to other factors, such as lifestyle choices.

- Research has shown that drinking too much tea can cause adverse effects, such as intestinal gas, nausea, heartburn, stomach pains, dizziness, or headaches.

- Herbal teas are also thought to contain their own beneficial properties. Ginkgo biloba, for example, has been shown in some studies to help manage anxiety, schizophrenia, and some forms of dementia. The U.S. Food and Drug Administration lists green tea with ginkgo biloba as an antioxidant that helps with mild memory problems.

- But not all herbal teas provide benefits. Yerba mate, for example, which was traditionally consumed in South America, is a popular drink. But Mayo Clinic warns that you should probably only enjoy it in moderation. Some studies found data to suggest that people who drink a lot of yerba mate over an extended period of time may be at increased risk of some types of cancer, such as that of the mouth, esophagus, and lungs.

Suggested Reading

King, *Tea, Coffee, & Chocolate*.
Standage, *A History of the World in 6 Glasses*.

Questions

1. What is the origin story of tea?

2. How was the Commutation Act of 1784 associated with U.S. history and tea consumption?

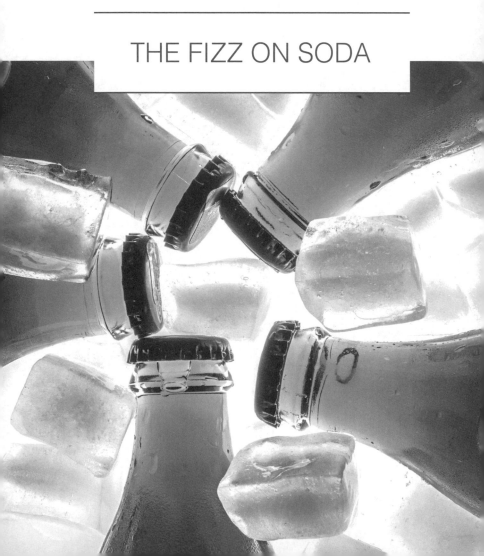

THE FIZZ ON SODA

Whether you call it soda, pop, soft drink, or soda water, this fizzy drink is an important part of world history. Once hailed as an embodiment of the American dream, it's now considered to be one of the worst contributors to obesity-related diseases. How did this drink come to be ubiquitous in every country in the world—and now contain so much controversy? That is the subject of this lecture.

The History of Soda

- Interestingly, the history of soda starts with mineral water. As ancient people discovered natural effervescent spring waters, they were fascinated with the fizzing element. Groups were divided: Either these special springs had healing properties or they were inhabited by evil spirits. This folklore lasted for centuries.

- In the 1600s, the mystery of fizzy water was finally solved. A Flemish scientist, Jan Baptista van Helmont, discovered carbon dioxide, the primary gas in effervescent water. A century later, Joseph Priestley, in 1767, set out to capture "fixed air" (carbon dioxide) from the fermentation process and add it to water.

- Priestley lived in Leeds next to a brewery. Taking advantage of the fermenting beer ingredients, he initially poured water back and forth in cups held over vats of beer. This became the first carbonated, or sparkling, water produced.

- We don't know for sure who the first people were to add flavoring to sparkling water, but it is said that in Tudor England and throughout Paris in the late 1600s, non-carbonated sodas or lemonades were very popular. Mixing carbonated water with syrup flavorings was happening in America by at least the early 1800s.

- These bottled carbonated drinks were quite popular, but sealing the bottle was a problem. None of the stoppers sealed the bottle properly; the fizz wouldn't stay put. Many different methods were tried but ultimately failed.

- Success did not come until the swing stopper was invented: A wire held the stopper in place and a wire lever allowed easy opening. However, the swing stopper was costly to make. It wasn't until 1892, when William Painter invented the crown cork bottle cap, that an effective and cheap way of bottle capping was found.

- For this method, the edges of the metal cap were crimped around the mouth of the bottle to keep it airtight. Painter also invented the Crown soda machine in 1898 that mixed the soda ingredients, bottled the liquid, and capped it all by machine, making it much faster than by hand.

- The first soda companies started out as patented medicines. Most of the big sodas that we are familiar with today were invented by pharmacists and sold in pharmacies; in fact, almost all of the soda fountains were housed in pharmacies. This was the case even when the purported medical benefits were highly debated.

Root Beer

- One of the first soft drinks to follow the trajectory from medicine to mass-marketed popular beverage was root beer.

- In medieval Europe, people would brew roots and herbs with the fizz of fermentation to cure a long list of ailments. These home-brew recipes followed immigrants to America. In the mid-1800s, entrepreneurs were looking for ways to sell root beer from stores and fountains.

- Henry Smith and Hiram Snow of New Hampshire found a way in 1866. Like the homemade brews, their concoction was carbonated through the fermentation process. It was called Smith's White Root Beer, and though it didn't achieve much success, it was patented.

- A more successful root beer maker was Quaker pharmacist Charles Elmer Hires, who opened his own drugstore and soda fountain in Philadelphia in the mid-1800s. Rumor has it that he was inspired by a lightly fermented herb tea that he had tried while on his honeymoon in New Jersey, so he decided to make and sell his own concoction.

- He prepared his brew with extract from roots, berries, bark, and herbs, calling it Hires Herbal Tea. But a friend advised him to change the name from "tea" to "root beer" to appeal to the working-class population of the city. With samples of his new Hires Root Beer, he introduced the product at the 1876 Philadelphia Centennial Exposition.

- Hires's root beer extract was sold in packets for 25 cents and could produce 5 gallons of the refreshment. All consumers had to do was add sugar, water, and yeast.

Dr Pepper

- Dr Pepper is another one of the oldest major soft drinks in the United States. It was created, manufactured, and sold beginning in 1885 in the central Texas town of Waco. Charles Alderton, a young pharmacist working at Morrison's Old Corner Drug Store, is believed to be the inventor of the now-famous drink.

- Alderton primarily worked mixing medicine at the pharmacy, which also had a soda fountain. He loved the smell of all the fruit syrups used to make carbonated sodas, so in his spare time, he served customers at the soda fountain. He began experimenting with different fruit syrup flavors, keeping a journal to document the different combinations. He finally hit on one recipe that satisfied him.

- Alderton first offered his unique concoction to the drugstore's owner, Wade Morrison, who liked the drink so much that he offered to sell it at his soda fountain. The soda was also a big hit with customers. According to the Dr Pepper Museum, Morrison is credited with naming the drink.

- As Dr Pepper grew in popularity, other soda fountains in town started buying the syrup and serving it. Soon, Alderton and Morrison could no longer keep up with demand. But Alderton was not interested in developing the soda further. He suggested that Morrison team up with Robert Lazenby, a young beverage chemist who liked the drink.

- Morrison and his new partner formed the Artesian Manufacturing and Bottling Company in 1891. In 1923, the company moved from Waco to Dallas. In 1904, at the world's fair exposition in Saint Louis, Dr Pepper was introduced to the world.

- The contents of the soda have been somewhat of a mystery. According to the senior vice president for research and development, the 23 flavors in Dr Pepper are so highly guarded that the recipe is hidden under lock and key inside a tightly secured vault hidden somewhere in the company's main building.

Coca-Cola

- The story of Coca-Cola starts with its inventor, John Pemberton. He moved to Atlanta, Georgia, in 1869 and opened up his own drugstore. By 1872, he was broke and heavily in debt.

- After spending several years paying off his debt, he started making patent medicines to sell throughout Atlanta. He happened to hear that coca leaves, what we know as the substance cocaine, had great positive energy effects, so he decided to give coca a try.

- At the time, a drink called Vin Mariani was wildly popular; it was a combination of wine and coca. Pemberton, in 1884, decided to make his own version of the coca wine and sell it. He claimed that it could cure all kinds of ills, including nerve damage, headaches, exhaustion, constipation, wasting disease, and more.

- Cocaine was not only legal then, but it was also in high demand. Pemberton's wine-coca business was a success, so in 1886, he founded Pemberton Chemical Company and started developing a product to sell to the soda fountains in town.

- Pemberton started making a syrup with coca leaves. To give his recipe an extra kick, he added another well-known drug, the kola nut, which is well known for its high caffeine content. The nut tasted bitter, however, so he added sugar—and lots of it—to mask the bitterness. Also into the mix went citric acid, a number of spices, and caramel to give it its signature deep-brown color.

- Pemberton gave a nearby soda fountain samples for their customers and then adjusted the formula according to their reactions. After trying the drink, Frank Robinson and David Doe, both in the advertising business, became convinced that Pemberton's soda would become a huge success and invested in the company

- Robinson and Doe then used their agency to advertise the new Coca-Cola (named after the coca leaf and kola nut ingredients). When the Pure Food and Drug Act of 1906 required all narcotics in a product to be labeled, Coca-Cola removed most of the cocaine from the drink. But it wasn't until 1929 that all traces of the drug were removed.

- When Pemberton's health started to fail, Doe left, but Robinson remained. He launched an advertising blitz that paid off and created the famous Coca-Cola logo.

- Pemberton, suffering from poor health and money problems, eventually sold all of his rights to the product to Asa Griggs Candler, a successful local pharmacist. Candler suffered from headaches, and Pemberton's former associate, Robinson, suggested he try a Coca-Cola. When it cured his headache several times, he was determined to buy the company, and did so in 1888. A few months later, Pemberton died. Candler brought Robinson back on for advertising.

- At the turn of the 20th century, the temperance movement was attempting to shut down alcohol consumption in America. As a result, more and more people left the bars for soda fountains. The soda industry aligned itself with temperance and was pleased as sales rose as a result of the movement and Prohibition.

- Coca-Cola began dominating the world market during World War II and only continued the trend of making its way to every corner of the globe. During World War II, the company offered to supply all American troops with a bottle of Coke for 5 cents. This won the hearts of American soldiers and made them very loyal to the brand.

- The sight of U.S. troops overseas drinking Coca-Colas helped the company expand to a global market and made Coke not only iconic, but a symbol of America. The international appeal of Coke is linked with its brilliant marketing strategy, which also led to what are called the soda wars—a battle between Coca-Cola and Pepsi that has persisted for decades.

7UP

- 7UP, the world's most beloved lime-flavored soda, has its roots in the Howdy Corporation in 1920. It was invented by Charles Leiper Grigg, who had previously created an orange soda called Whistle.

- Until 1950, 7UP contained lithium citrate, which is a mood stabilizer used in the psychiatric treatment of several disorders, such as bipolarity. Coca-Cola also had a version that contained lithium.

- The 7UP name may come from the 7 ingredients: carbonated water, sugar, citric acid, citric oils, sodium citrate, and lithium citrate. The "UP" portion of the name might refer to the fact that people had a lifted mood after imbibing it. But Grigg is rumored to have taken the secret of the origins of the soda's abbreviated name to the grave.

- 7UP introduced one of the first diet sodas, originally called Like and introduced in 1963. It was only on the market for 6 years, however, as the sweetener used—cyclamate—was then banned by the U.S. government.

Health Concerns

- Soft drinks are increasingly linked with obesity and other health issues, such as cavity formation. A 2-liter bottle of soda contains about 54 teaspoons of sugar while a 12-oz can of soda typically contains about 10 teaspoons of sugar—which amounts to 140 and 150 calories respectively. All of soda's calories come from sugar. It is due to this high sugar content that soda is now considered to be a main contributor to the global obesity pandemic.

- Health concerns focus almost entirely on sugar content, because most sodas are low in caffeine. Sodas are made with sucrose (table sugar) and high-fructose corn syrup. Research shows that excessive sugar consumption from any source correlates with obesity.

- Cutting down on sugar is associated with weight loss while eating more sugar is associated with obesity, type 2 diabetes, heart disease, stroke, and other ailments.

- Diet sodas do not contain sugar and are instead sweetened with artificial sweeteners, such as aspartame. The U.S. Food and Drug Administration says that these sweeteners are safe, especially in small amounts. But others argue that when consumed in large amounts, they fool the body into thinking it is sugar, stimulate insulin release, and raise the risk for obesity and type 2 diabetes.

- However, there is not enough research at this time to determine any long-term effects of consuming diet drinks. It is evident that diet sodas don't help most people control portions or their weight.

- Along with new policies that restrict where sodas are sold, our growing awareness of soda's unhealthy impact is hurting soda sales. Although the carbonated soft drink remains a remarkably American beverage, statistics show a decline in American soda purchases over the last few years.

Suggested Reading

Donovan, *Fizz*.
Standage, *A History of the World in 6 Glasses*.

Questions

1. What is the historical link between soda and medicinal tonics?

2. How did the Pure Food and Drug Act of 1906 affect the ingredients used in cola beverages, such as Coca-Cola?

LECTURE
21

FOOD AS RITUAL

Eating is essential to survival, but what we eat, how we eat, and where and when we eat are based on ecology, available resources, cultural variation, and temporal space. Eating is also deeply symbolic and is associated with rituals all around the world. This lecture will explore the world history of food as ritual—which can be defined as emotionally meaningful or significant activities that one performs in a set way, whether as a routine sequence or in association with a particular event.

Religious Ceremonies

- Libation in ancient Egypt, Greece, and Rome was a vital aspect of religious practice. The practice involved making liquid offerings—using water, wine, or milk and honey—to deities or to honor the dead.

- Beyond libation and its link to religious practice, there are many other examples of the way that food is ritualized in religious practice. The Jewish Sabbath is just one example. The Sabbath is Judaism's seventh day of the week, a day of rest where people are supposed to relax and refrain from working.

- According to Jewish religious law, Sabbath is observed from right before sunset on Friday evening to the first appearance of 3 stars in the sky on Saturday night. During this time, 3 meals are eaten. The first meal is Friday dinner, the second is Saturday lunch, and the third is late in the afternoon on Saturday.

- The first 2 meals are typically lavishly prepared and include special dishes, such as challah bread, a braided egg-based bread. These first 2 meals also open with the kiddush, a Jewish blessing, which is recited over a cup of wine. This is followed by blessing the challah, which begins the meal. The head of the household slices the bread, and everyone eats a piece dipped in salt.

- Seder is another holy meal in the Jewish faith that is highly ritualized. It marks the beginning of Passover and involves the retelling of the story of the liberation of the Israelites from slavery in Egypt. It typically involves drinking wine and eating symbolic foods, such as matzah, an unleavened flatbread.

- In other religions, sacred meals also play a big role. In Catholicism, for example, as well as many other Protestant religions, the Holy Communion is a religious ritual that is considered to be a sacrament. It is also called the Eucharist and involves consecrating bread and wine on an altar or communion table and then consuming them. The Priest turns the bread and wine symbolically into the body and blood of Christ, a highly ritualized act that is punctuated with consumption of food and drink.

- Religions all over the world are also associated with many food restrictions. Buddhism, for example, is often linked with veganism

and vegetarianism. The principle of ahimsa includes avoiding eating foods where any harm was done.

- Other religions that also urge vegetarian or vegan diets include Hinduism and Rastafarianism. Those that adhere to the principles of the Rastafari movement, for example, consume foods that are called Ital. There are a few different versions of this diet, but it loosely means choosing foods that are as natural and unprocessed as possible.

- Hinduism is one of the oldest religions in the world and today is characterized by vegetarianism, even though originally, in ancient India, meat was not prohibited. And while avoiding meat is central to some Indian religions, such as Jainism, it is conditionally accepted in contemporary Hindu practices.

- Islamic food practices also involve avoiding certain foods. Some foods are categorized as halal, meaning those that can be eaten, and as haram, foods that should be avoided. These foods to be avoided include animals not slaughtered in the Islamic way, pork or any products using any pork by-products, alcohol, or any blood or blood by-products.

- Fasting is another central part of the Muslim religion. During the month of Ramadan, which is the 9th month in the Islamic calendar, practitioners refrain from eating or drinking from dawn until sunset.

- People who practice Jainism can choose to fast at any time but most often do it during religious holy days. They not only stop eating, but they also aim to stop desiring to eat.

- There are several types of fasting: complete, partial, or simply giving up your favorite foods. Many Christians all around the world give up something during their season of reflection and penance, Lent, which starts on Ash Wednesday and takes place during the 46 days before Easter Sunday.

- On the other end of the spectrum, feasting is also a major component of many religious practices. In the Czech Republic at Easter, people eat many traditional holiday foods, including smoked meat, eggs and fresh nettle, sweet cakes called *mazanec*, and sweet dessert cakes baked into the shape of a lamb. Many of their traditional festivals are based in ancient pagan traditions.

- Easter traditions that are relished in the United States also have deep roots in paganism. Many ancient Pagan rituals centered around the spring, or vernal, equinox. This occurs when the Sun crosses the celestial equator, the imaginary line above the Earth's equator.

- The name "Easter," as well as how Americans came to associate bunnies and eggs with the resurrection of Christ, come from the Germanic goddess Eostre. A fertility goddess, her sacred animal is the rabbit, and eggs are a sign of fertility and rebirth.

Halloween

- Another holiday that has pagan roots and underscores the link between food and ritual is Halloween. Many think that this holiday has roots in the ancient Celtic festival of Samhain, which marks the end of the harvest season and the beginning of the "darker" part of the year.

- This time is seen as transitional—not only in terms of the weather, but also in terms of the distances between the living world and the otherworld or underworld. It was during this time that the ghosts of the dead were thought to return to the Earth.

- In about the 9th century, the Latin Church of the Roman Catholic Church shifted the date of All Hallows, or Day of the Saints, to November 1. The vigil for the festival was October 31. November 2 later became All Souls Day, when people commemorated the dearly departed. All 3 of these days are still celebrated throughout Mexico today, with slight variation.

- On November 2, called Day of the Dead, families go to the cemetery to decorate the tombstones of their deceased loved ones. They eat special bread, translated into "bread of the dead," a sweet roll or bun. Another food that is associated with Day of the Dead is sugar skulls, which are meant to represent the departed person and often have their name inscribed on the forehead.

- In the United States, Day of the Dead celebrations are increasing in popularity. But the most commonly celebrated version of Day of the Saints or All Hallows is Halloween, which is celebrated on October 31: All Hallows Eve.

- Halloween in the United States was historically a celebration day when people would come together and celebrate the harvest and tell stories of the dead—not that dissimilar from Samhain. The dressing up in costume, which was originally part of the Celtic celebration, began to enter into popular American celebrations of the holiday in the second half of the 19th century.

- The tradition of dressing up and going door to door is said to have started during the Middle Ages. According to the Smithsonian, most often children, but occasionally poor adults, would dress up in costumes and go door to door begging for money or food in exchange for prayers and songs said on behalf of the deceased.

- Creating jack-o'-lanterns and bobbing for apples are traditions with ancient roots. Bobbing for apples is a custom that is associated with a Roman tradition of honoring Pomona, the goddess of fruit, who is represented by an apple.

- Carving pumpkins into jack-o'-lanterns is a tradition that dates back hundreds of years. The original tradition in Ireland and Scotland involved people carving faces into gourds and turnips to ward away wandering spirits who might be passing by their doors on All Hallow's Eve. When immigrants moved to America, they brought their traditions with them and soon found that pumpkins, a squash plant native to North America, made perfect jack-o'-lanterns.

Thanksgiving

- Another American holiday that is certainly associated with ritual is Thanksgiving. In 1621, colonists from Plymouth, Massachusetts, shared a meal with Native Americans from the Wampanoag tribe. While some might think that this was the first Thanksgiving meal, historians have pointed to an even earlier beginning of the tradition.

- According to the National Constitution Center, a history museum based in Philadelphia, the history of Thanksgiving actually begins in 1541, when Spanish explorer Francisco Vásquez de Coronado held a Thanksgiving feast for his half-starved men during a long journey in what is present-day Texas.

- In 1619, another historic meal of thanks occurred in Berkeley Plantation, Virginia, by the initial settlers. Thanksgiving meant to take some time to give thanks to god and community.

- In 1620, Pilgrims moved to Massachusetts. The first year in the colonies was particularly rough on the settlers. In 1621, the colonists were introduced to a Native American man the history books call Squanto.

- His birth name was Tisquantum, and he was a member of the Pawtuxet band of the Wampanoag. He had been kidnapped years earlier, traveled to Europe, and spoke English fluently. He eventually made it back to North America, only to find that his tribe had nearly all died of disease.

- Squanto began living with and assisting the Plymouth Pilgrims, as they were dying and very undernourished. He taught them how to plant northern flint corn, which was hearty and would flourish in the climate.

- That fall, the pilgrims held a multiday feast to give thanks to god and to the harvest. This tradition was something they brought with them from the old country, but with a new twist: They invited Squanto and the Wampanoag to join them.

- The spread of food that they offered looked very different from what we have come to expect at our Thanksgiving table today. They did feast on roast turkey, but they also ate roast goose, codfish, lobster, eel, and clams. Their guests brought 5 deer and shared the venison. From then on, the colonies began celebrating harvest with large meals.

- Until 1777, the celebration was confined to the New England area. The first Thanksgiving that was celebrated nationwide was in response to a military victory during the Revolutionary War.

- After this time, westward expansion began, and people—and their customs—began moving to new territories. They brought the Thanksgiving tradition with them. And in 1863, Thanksgiving was made a national holiday by President Abraham Lincoln.

- The large festive meals were not always good for the native peoples who participated in them, and there were many massacres of Indian tribes associated with the feasts. Despite the darker side of the history, Thanksgiving is one of the most popular and commonly celebrated holidays in the United States.

- Thanksgiving has many rituals associated with it, not the least of which is the turkey. It meets all of the criteria for a ritual sacrifice and is even replete with the famous "pardoning" of a turkey done by the American President every year. We also tend to associate pies, cranberry sauce, stuffing, and mashed potatoes with the holiday—and these are just a few of the culinary traditions.

- Perhaps one of the most well-known characteristics of the Thanksgiving ritual is overstuffing ourselves. And many people feel sleepy after eating a giant meal—something that is often erroneously linked to something called tryptophan in the turkey. Nutrition researchers and neuroscientists have come to an agreement: It isn't the tryptophan in your turkey that is making you sleepy; it is simply that you have overeaten, which has a sedative effect.

Suggested Reading

Visser, *The Rituals of Dinner*.

Questions

1. What is one example of how fasting is related to ritual?

2. How is ritual associated with many of our holiday culinary rituals in the United States?

LECTURE
22

WHEN PEOPLE
EAT THINGS THAT
AREN'T FOOD

This lecture will examine the circumstances surrounding why people consume things that are not considered to be food items by tracing some of these practices across cultures. Whether in the form of a nutrient deficiency, an eating disorder, a funeral rite, a way to express dominance over your enemy, or as a medical treatment, people all around the world eat the most curious nonfood items.

Pica

- Some of the strangest things that people have been reported eating include a cell phone, a lighter, and a 14-pound hair ball. This last example was from a woman who ate her own hair. She suffered from a condition called trichotillomania, which is the compulsion to pull out your own hair, and tricophagia, which is the compulsion to eat it.

- This behavior is part of a larger category of behaviors that doctors call pica, the word used to describe an appetite or craving for substances that are not nutritive, such as paper, metal, glass, coffee grounds, rust, and so on.

- It is considered to be an eating disorder and is found more often in kids rather than adults. For the pattern to be diagnosed as pica, people typically have to eat the item or items for at least a month. And sometimes the practice can last years.

- The Centers for Disease Control report that hospitalizations due to pica are on the rise. And some instances, outside of short-term cravings or eating disorders, involve performance art. One famous example of pica is where a man intentionally consumed metal—for years. French entertainer Michel Lotito famously ate a Cesna 150 airplane in the late 1970s. The process took him about 2 years.

● Todd Robbins, a very well-known magician and lecturer, began swallowing swords at a Coney Island amusement park in the early 1980s. Sword swallowing is not eating, per se. It is essentially placing a sword into your mouth, relaxing your esophageal muscles, and passing the sword through your digestive tract.

Geophagia

● People are also known to crave nonfood items. One of the most popular types of pica is called geophagy or geophagia, the consumption of soil, clay, or chalk.

● Some nutrition research suggests that eating certain soils or clays can make foods that contain poisonous chemical compounds edible. Another functional benefit of geophagy is thought to be linked with balancing mineral and trace-element deficiencies.

● Geophagy is common in nonhuman animals all over the world and throughout history. Some paleoanthropologists have claimed that the discovery of calcium-rich white clay beside the skeletal remains of early human ancestors suggests that geophagy is a practice with deep evolutionary roots.

● Although impossible to prove, it seems very likely that our ancestors may have intentionally ingested silica or clay in an attempt to meet micronutrient deficiencies. Even in historical texts, we see references to geophagy.

● But it is not just a historical practice; people all around the world still eat soil and clay. And while the mineral content can vary, depending on geographic region, most soils contain calcium, copper, iron, zinc, and magnesium.

- Some believe that these are good sources for pregnant women or people who don't typically have access to proper nutrition. The clay may actually absorb critical nutrients that your body needs, which can be very dangerous for pregnant women. Despite the lack of medical consensus, people still like eating dirt.

Pagophagia and Other Pregnancy Cravings

- Women in many cultures are reported to crave certain foods during pregnancy. Chewing ice, for example, is a common one. The practice, called pagophagia, has long been associated with iron-deficiency anemia. Although, according to Mayo Clinic, the reasons for this association are still unclear. One study, led by psychologist Melissa Hunt, found that ice chewing might increase alertness in people who are anemic.

- Other cravings reported by pregnant women include everything ranging from sweets, to meat, to the stereotypical pickles and ice cream. A 2015 study in Ireland found that about 40% of the participants reported food cravings, with sweets, fruit, and dairy products as the most commonly craved items. Women from different parts of the world crave different foods.

- There are a number of different hypotheses as to why women might have cravings during their pregnancies. Some suggest that women who have cravings have desires to eat such foods even when they're not pregnant, reflecting simply a desire to eat more.

- Some suggest that the cravings are brought on by hormonal changes associated with pregnancy. And some believe that this behavior is linked to increased smell and taste sensitivity during pregnancy, which also might associate with food aversions.

Placentophagy

- Another unusual thing that women ingest is something that they eat after giving birth. It's a practice is called placentophagy. Placenta is an organ grown in the uterus of a female mammal that connects mother to baby via the umbilical cord.

- Oxygen and nutrients pass from the maternal blood supply into the placenta and are carried by the umbilical cord to the unborn gestating fetus. It also functions to remove waste products from the baby, such as carbon dioxide, that travel back along the umbilical cord to the placenta and then into the mother's bloodstream, where her body easily disposes of the waste.

- The umbilical cord plays a crucial role during pregnancy and is the lifeline between baby and mother, and many people believe that it also has a beneficial role to play after the baby is born. The practice of placentophagy is the consumption of the placenta postpartum.

- Most mammals on Earth eat their placenta after birth. There is some debate among researchers about why animals engage in this process, but many think that they do it because they gain some benefits. These benefits include analgesic effects, or reduction in pain, and might be linked to oxytocin, a hormone present in placenta.

- There is also a school of thought that believes that mammalian mothers eat their placenta as a way to clean the area and remove waste so that predators aren't attracted to the birth site. Whatever the ultimate causation, it is quite common in the wild.

- While there is a long-standing belief that many small-scale societies around the world engage in the practice, there is scant evidence that that's actually true. Today, the practice is becoming

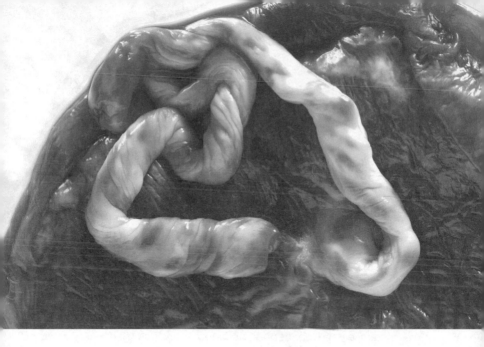

widespread among women in the postindustrialized West, largely based on the unsubstantiated idea that indigenous peoples do it.

- Women eat their placenta in a variety of ways. The bravest ones consume it raw, while others bake it into a meal, such as eggplant parmesan or lasagna, or steep it into a liquid. The vast majority, however, choose to eat their placenta in the form of dehydrated pills.

- The women who ingest their placenta report that it helps them combat baby blues, increases their breast milk production, reduces stress, and restores iron. It is important to note, however, that there is currently no scientific evidence to support the claims that are made.

- Despite the increasing popularity of the trend, however, the practice of human placentophagy remains quite controversial.

Anthropophagy

- Cannibalism is also called anthropophagy, the consumption of human flesh or internal organs by other human beings. Historically, many different societies have practiced cannibalism, although the practice is very rare today. Many historians and religious scholars believe that as Western religion, law, and customs have spread to preindustrial societies, the practice diminished and then largely disappeared.

- Some paleoanthropologists—scholars who study the behavioral and biological evolution of our ancestors—think that the practice goes all the way back to the Paleolithic period. Neanderthal remains from France, dating to about 100,000 years ago, were discovered in the 1990s that many scientists claim showed evidence of cannibalism.

- Evidence for Neanderthal anthropophagy has also been found at sites in Spain. And more recently, in 2016, excavations from Belgium yielded human remains that show evidence of butchery, which many associate with cannibalism.

- The way that they identify cannibalism is typically by looking at the human bones that they pull out of the ground. When the bones have deliberate cut marks in a certain pattern, the experts can show evidence that the bones were de-fleshed. Some types of cut marks can also be identified as indicating dismemberment.

- The Middle Ages saw quite a bit of cannibalism all around the world. Medieval doctors, for example, used to grind up Egyptian mummies and sell the powder. It was thought to cure a wide range of ailments, from headaches to stomach pains.

- The idea that mummy powder could cure ailments stems from the practice of using bitumen for arthritis, cataracts, and even leprosy.

Bitumen is a sort of naturally occurring tar of petroleum jelly and could be harvested from the Dead Sea.

- Apothecaries would pay a premium to get Egyptian mummy powder, and it is thought that the powder was sold from the 12th to the 17th century. Historians claim, however, that when mummies were in short supply—or, in fact, impossible to get—any cadaver would do.

- Mummy powder was not the only cure used by apothecaries to treat illness and disease. Rendered human fat, blood, and even certain organs (such as the liver) were all harvested, packaged, and sold as medical treatments.

- Outside of the apothecary shops, other evidence of cannibalism occurred in different contexts all around the world. One interesting practice is called endocannibalism and is essentially a funerary rite. Tribes such as the Aghori of India, the Amahuaca of Peru, and the Fore of Papua New Guinea would historically engage in mortuary cannibalism. There is some variation, but it largely involves eating part of the remains, whether that is some of the bone, ashes, or flesh of the departed.

- The key part of this practice is that you are consuming someone who is part of your social group or community. The opposite of endocannibalism, then, is the practice of exocannibalism—eating someone outside of your social group (such as your enemy).

- Examples of cultures that historically engaged in this practice include the Wari of Brazil, the Batak of Indonesia, the Aztecs of Mexico, and the Iroquois of the United States. The practice was meant to express hostility and dominance.

- Other forms of exocannibalism may include sociopathic practices, where a person consumes his or her victim as the final act of violence. But how this type of cannibalism is classified is debated among researchers who study death and dying in all of its forms.

- Outside of ritual cannibalism, there is also what is called survival cannibalism. This type of anthropophagy involves consuming human flesh in emergency situations or in cases of extreme hunger, such as starvation. Some of the most famous instances in history include the 1846 Donner Party in the Sierra Nevada and the South American athletes who were stranded in the Andes in 1972.

- Today, you don't hear about cases of cannibalism too often. A recent *Smithsonian* magazine article, however, suggests that some ethnic groups in Papua New Guinea might still be engaging in the practice on a limited basis. If the practice is still happening, experts say it is rare and must be kept quiet. This information is highly contested, however.

Suggested Reading

Schutt, *Cannibalism*.
Young, *Craving Earth*.

Questions

1. What is pica?

2. How has cannibalism (in its many forms) been associated with human consumption patterns throughout history?

LECTURE
23

FOOD AS RECREATIONAL DRUGS

When most people think of food, it might seem like a straightforward and clear definition of what differentiates food from other consumables. But the boundaries that separate food for nourishment versus things we eat as food are culturally determined and can easily blur. This is the case when exploring food as recreational drugs. Throughout human history and around the world, people have been consuming foods not only for the nourishment, but also for the psychological effects.

Hallucinogenic Mushrooms

- Humans have had a long history with psilocybin, or hallucinogenic mushrooms, with evidence dating back to the Aztecs. During pre-Columbian times, the mushrooms we now know as psilocybin were called god's flesh by the Aztecs. The Mexican mushroom had cult status among natives, and even the Spanish conquest in the 16th century didn't disrupt mushroom worship.

- The effects of the sacred mushroom were known to shamans and healers, who believed that the mushroom's power would be diminished or used in a profane way if it fell into the hands of a white man. So, they kept it a tightly guarded secret from nonnatives until the beginning of the 20th century.

- It was at this point that anthropologists reported that native Mexicans consumed mushrooms as a means to put themselves in touch with the gods and provide guiding hallucinations and mystical knowledge.

- But it wasn't until *Life* magazine published an article in 1957 that Americans discovered the spiritual mushrooms. The article, titled, "The Discovery of Mushrooms That Cause Strange Visions," was the first account from a Westerner, Robert Gordon Wasson, who had actually experienced the Mexican mushrooms. The article gave not only a description of the "trip" but also came complete with photos and drawings. American readers were stunned by the ethereal effects.

- Wasson's article was the impetus for experimentation with hallucinogens in the 1960s. The counterculture at that time believed that drugs such as psilocybin (the active ingredient in the mushrooms) and LSD brought the mind and spirit together in the quest for transcendental knowledge.

- Wasson's book, *Mushrooms, Russia and History*, was published at the same time that the *Life* article was released. The book describes the study of the role that mushrooms play in different cultures by him and his wife, and it eventually led them to its practice in Mexico.

- Mexican Indians referred to psilocybin mushrooms with awe and reverence; they were never to be taken lightly. In decades to come, these magic mushrooms would inspire artists, intellectuals, and spiritual seekers.

- While psilocybin had been documented before, it wasn't until Wasson's study was published that historians gave any credit to the role of psychedelic agents. They finally started to understand that these mushrooms had tremendous psychological power over the people who consumed them, and it helped shape their belief systems within their cultures

- Today, psilocybin mushrooms are illegal in the United States, but Western travelers to places such as Indonesia, Thailand, and Bali can easily buy mushroom omelets and cola-mushroom shakes from the locals.

- Psychoactive fungi have been used since ancient times in religious ceremonies. Plato drank mushroom tea at the Greek rites of Eleusis, and mushrooms were eaten by the Celts and their druid priests, by the Vikings, and later by medieval witches.

- At low to moderate doses, psilocybin mushrooms make colors seem brighter, more saturated, and better defined. At very high doses, the consumer could easily lose touch with all reality and dissolve into a world of color and form.

- Reports suggest that most people ingest moderate doses and have a pleasant experience. But some people have negative hallucinations and can experience headaches, sweating, chills, and nausea.

- The toxicity level is low in psilocybin mushrooms, so some suggest this means that it would be very difficult for someone to die by ingesting them. Furthermore, some believe that mushrooms aren't addictive, but that remains controversial.

Cannabis

- With marijuana becoming legal in some states in the United States, the sale of edible treats has risen. There is a growing preference for marijuana edibles among patients and recreational users alike.

- Many marijuana dispensaries look like cannabis candy stores and bakeries, where one can find everything from salad dressings and dips to gummy bears and cookies. In fact, you can infuse cannabis into just about any recipe that you can think of that includes butter or oil.

- Actually, edible marijuana has been around for a while. Brownies made with marijuana have remained popular since the 1950s, likely because chocolate is very effective at covering up the marijuana taste.

- Evidence points to ancient people almost exclusively eating marijuana, rather than smoking it. They saved the seeds for food and ate the flowers for medicinal, recreational, and spiritual use.

- In the 1960s and 1970s, so-called pot-smoking hippies became vegetarians and sought ethnic foods that were unheard of in the United States, such as tofu, seaweed, curries, hummus, and burritos. This counterculture cuisine favored by health-food junkies provided the basis for the local food movement seen today based on organic, sustainable foods.

- There's now a "stoner cuisine" movement centered around the idea of creating unusual combinations of food and pairing unusual

flavors while high on marijuana. Edible-marijuana cookbooks abound and include not only recipes but also tantalizing photos of scrumptious food.

- Even though New York is not one of the United States that has legalized marijuana for recreational use (yet), that hasn't stopped a new trend in the city: marijuana restaurants. With legalization taking off, marijuana restaurants could be the new culinary craze.

- In 1996, when California legalized medical marijuana, it opened the door for edible marijuana. Patients can ingest cannabis without damaging their lungs and without the smell of smoke on their hands and clothes, and they can use it more discreetly.

- Recreational users can catch a high by consuming marijuana without the stoner stigma attached to smoking it. Both are finding the benefits of eating their herb, including a longer-lasting high for body and mind.

- Like wine tasting, cigar smoking, and gourmet cooking, pot also has differentiating smells for the aficionado. Terpenes, which are hydrocarbons found in the essential oils of plants, give pot and other foods their unique aroma and taste. Pairing the terpene of a certain marijuana strain with a food that has the same terpene is argued to make an unforgettable combination.

- The culinary community has also noted the rise in popularity of marijuana edibles and now offers cooking classes in certain states devoted to cooking with marijuana.

- Eating edible marijuana treats causes a wide range of effects. Most people feel a combination of one or more of the following effects: euphoria, sedation, relaxation, possibly paranoia, anxiety, and increased appetite. Eating too much, however, is reported to be a very unpleasant experience (although not fatal) and can cause nausea, dizziness, extreme anxiety, and even hallucinations.

- Edibles may be popular items at dispensaries, but because the federal government still considers marijuana illegal, there are no universal standards in place for marijuana edibles. But the number of states that have legalized cannabis either for medical use and/or recreational use is growing considerably, and standardized testing is on the horizon.

Food Addiction

- The satisfaction and joy that you can get from your favorite foods can be a real high for many people. Of course, we get energy from food intake, but it's much more than that—it can be one of the greatest pleasures of our lives.

- Studies have shown that food affects the pleasure centers in our brain the same way that drugs do, so there can be potential problems with overeating, just like drug abuse. But it's also been shown that food can make people happy, at least temporarily.

- Certain herbs, spices, and aromatics used in the kitchen can have a direct effect on mood. For example, orange, rosemary, and lemon are argued to help energize. Lavender and sage are thought to be great stress relievers. And some argue that chamomile can ease insomnia, while mint and basil are thought to be mood boosting.

- Mood-affecting neurotransmitters in the brain are created by food compounds. Some foods are better at helping neurotransmitter production than others and therefore affect mood to a greater extent.

- Foods linked to stress relief include dark chocolate, turkey, walnuts, sweet potatoes, almonds, spinach, and salmon. There is no way to know whether there is a direct link between eating the foods and a reduction in stress, but many food aficionados are convinced.

- New research shows that our brains can view delicious foods as drugs. Ice cream and other high-calorie foods can elicit cravings and trigger responses similar to those caused by addictive drugs, such as cocaine.

- Some studies have shown that certain foods trigger a reward center in the brain. Other studies show that certain foods trigger similar brain patterns to those of addictive drugs. Research on obesity continues to probe a similar link. The difficulty is differentiating between brain scans that show addiction, cravings, and pleasure.

- Some recent studies show that highly processed foods share properties with drugs of abuse due to their fat content and/ or refined carbohydrates, along with the rapid rate that refined carbohydrates are absorbed in the system.

- Food addiction is characterized by loss of control over consumption, continued use despite negative consequences, and an inability to cut down despite the desire to do so. Addictive-like eating has been associated with an increase in impulse and emotional reaction, which are similar to substance abuse—in other words, they share common behavioral patterns.

- Food addiction typically happens when a person is predisposed to addictive behavior and the food itself contains an addictive agent. Most addictive foods have been altered or processed in a way that increases their abuse potential.

- There are naturally occurring foods that contain sugar, which is refined carbohydrates, such as fruit, and those that naturally contain fat, such as nuts, but rarely does a food contain both. However, palatable, processed foods have been altered to contain elevated amounts of both—for example, cake, pizza, and chocolate bars. There has also been a steep increase in the availability of these highly processed foods.

- Like drugs of abuse, highly processed foods have been made to trigger addictive-like biological and behavioral responses due to their high reward level. And both contain a higher dose of addictive ingredients.

- Addictive substances—both food and drugs—have been processed to increase the rate at which the addictive substance is absorbed into the blood. Highly processed foods are likely to cause a blood-sugar spike, and it's been shown that there's a link between glucose levels and the activation of parts of the brain that are involved with addiction.

- Doing drugs, just like overeating junk food, causes the brain's pleasure centers to overload. Eventually, the pleasure centers reach a plateau, so to feel the same pleasure, a person has to increase the amount of food or drugs.

Suggested Reading

Bone, *Mycophilia*.
McKenna, *Food of the Gods*.

Questions

1. What is psilocybin, and how does it illustrate the blurred boundaries between food and recreational drugs?

2. How has the recent legalization of marijuana influenced culinary practices at some high-end restaurants in urban areas?

FOOD AS MEDICINE

For most of human history, foods have been more than just sources of nutrition. They are part of cultural identity and ritual practices and are used all around the world as medicinal remedies. This lecture will explore several foods that were historically touted as having medicinal properties that are also currently under investigation using modern medical research techniques. Historically, the boundary separating food and medicinal drugs was blurred. Today, the debate about whether food can actually act as medicine rages on.

Ancient Greek Medicine

Hippocrates

- Hippocrates is hailed as one of the most influential figures in the history of medicine, and much of his medical advice stemmed from the idea that a healthy diet could be healing.

- There were 3 branches of medicine in ancient Greece: pharmacology, surgery, and dietetics. Dietetics, which included diet, exercise, and sexual activity, is thought to have been the most prestigious branch of medicine at the time.

- In Greece during the classical period, Hippocrates practiced medicine based on the 4 humors. It was the idea that the human body is filled with 4 basic substances, called humors, which are in balance when a person is healthy.

- They were based on the 4 elements of earth, water, air, and fire and represented the substances in one's body. They also represented the qualities of hot, cold, wet, and dry, and each was associated with a corresponding temperament.

1. The first humor is phlegm. It's embodied by the temperament phlegmatic, meaning calm, and represents the element water and the qualities of cold and wet.

2. The second humor is yellow bile. It's embodied by the temperament choleric, or irritable, and represents the element fire and the qualities hot and dry.

3. The third humor is blood, embodied by the temperament sanguine, or optimistic, and representing the element air and the qualities hot and wet.

4. The fourth humor is black bile, embodied by the temperament melancholic, or gloomy, and representing the element earth and the qualities cold and dry.

● The humors were the basis for much of Greek medicine, and medical practitioners of the day believed that they were intricately tied to food. Practices involved assessing the temperament of the food and then eating accordingly to remedy ills and imbalances.

● All foods had a nature and temperament, and medicine acted on polarities.

1. The first polarity was hot/cold. Foods that were considered hot acted to stimulate the metabolism. Some foods in this category include horseradish, onions, ginger, garlic, and aged cheese. Cool foods, those that were thought to slow down metabolism, included such things as milk and dairy products, bananas, watermelon, and cucumbers.

2. The second polarity was wet/dry. Wet foods were thought to be emollient or soothing. These included similar foods

to those in the cool category. Dry foods, on the other hand, were thought to help absorb excess fluids in the body. These included beans, dried fruits, and aged cheeses.

- In addition to these polarities, each humor was thought to have food that aggravated it. Medical practitioners took great care in prescribing foods to address the medical condition at hand.

Garlic

- While garlic is primarily used as a flavoring, it is increasingly being touted as a nutritional supplement with beneficial properties.

- Recently, a large meta-analysis reviewed evidence from 20 clinical trials with almost 1000 participants, summarizing the current data on the health effects of garlic, and showed that garlic can have cardiovascular protective and immunomodulatory properties. This means that there is evidence to suggest that it can be used to lower blood pressure, regulate slightly elevated cholesterol, and stimulate the immune system.

- While promising data from clinical trials has shown that garlic has potential benefits for heart health, such as lowering blood pressure, Mayo Clinic warns that the research is still preliminary and cautions people to avoid using garlic supplements as their only approach.

- There is also some exciting new research to suggest that garlic may help reduce cancer risk. The results from clinical trials for garlic are mixed—but ongoing. Given this, the National Institutes of Health (NIH) doesn't currently recommend any dietary supplement for the prevention of cancer. Based on the promising data, however, it does recognize garlic as having potential anticancer properties.

- These are likely linked to the presence of an antioxidant in garlic. An antioxidant is either a synthetically produced or naturally occurring substance that may prevent or slow down some types of cell damage. Antioxidants are found in many different plant foods, including garlic.

Turmeric

- Turmeric is also known as Indian saffron and is a member of the ginger family. Turmeric has a long history of use in Ayurvedic medicine, an ancient Indian system of natural healing. It is one of the world's oldest medical systems and is thought to be 3000 to 4000 years old.

- Central to Ayurveda, much as in humoral medicine practiced by the Greeks, is the idea that the use of herbal compounds and special diets can promote health. Turmeric has been listed as part of Ayurvedic medicine and is thought to promote digestion, have positive benefits for the heart and circulatory system, and support the brain and nervous system.

- Ayurvedic medicine isn't widely recognized or studied as part of conventional Western medicine, but they do share some supplements in common, such as turmeric.

- Turmeric contains curcumin, a chemical produced by the plant that has antioxidant properties. The results of clinical trials are promising for a wide variety of diseases, including cardiovascular disease, arthritis, Crohn's disease, colitis, irritable bowel disease, and peptic ulcers. There is also some promising evidence that curcumin can help control diabetes and even reduce the risk of some forms of cancer.

Ginger

- While commonly used in cooking to add flavor, ginger has long been thought to cure various ailments, such as nausea, motion sickness, and other digestive issues.

- Traditional Chinese medicine (TCM), which possibly dates back to around 4000 or 5000 years, has long claimed that ginger is a miracle root.

- Much of TCM practices are linked with herbal supplements. And like Ayurveda, TCM is not generally considered as part of Western medical treatment. Some health practitioners, however, encourage TCM as a complementary health approach.

- Ginger is also listed as a beneficial medical treatment in ancient Greek medicine.

- Based on medical research over the last few decades, we know that there are more than 100 constituents in ginger that might be linked to positive digestive health outcomes, might help control diabetes, and might potentially reduce cancer risk.

- Ginger has also been shown to have beneficial effects for rheumatoid arthritis, respiratory issues, and migraines. Despite these promising results, ginger has yet to be proven effective.

Cinnamon

- Cinnamon also shares a history of being used in TCM. It was used for treating respiratory, digestive, and gynecological ailments.

- There are 2 different types of cinnamon: cassia cinnamon, from China, and Ceylon cinnamon (called true cinnamon), from Sri Lanka.

- Research has looked at the effects of cinnamon supplements on controlling blood sugar and as a treatment for multiple sclerosis, an autoimmune disorder. The results, while promising, are sparse.

- In 2012, a meta-analysis of 10 clinical trials in people with type 1 or type 2 diabetes found that cinnamon didn't effectively reduce levels of glucose or glycosylated hemoglobin A1c (HbA1c), which is a measure of blood sugar control. Based on this, the NIH does not encourage the use of cinnamon for any health condition.

Goji Berries

- Another ancient medical system that blurred the boundaries between medicine and food were the ancient Aztecs. Much of their medical practice was driven by magic, sorcery, and their religious beliefs, but it turns out that for some of these plants, there is evidence to suggest that they might be effective.

- One of these is goji berries, or wolf berries. The little fruits were used historically to treat conditions such as fever and were also thought to be an antiaging drug. Today, their touted benefits include treating such health conditions as high blood pressure, diabetes, and age-related eye problems.

- Goji berries contain antioxidants and betaine, an amino acid that is involved with liver function, cellular reproduction, and helping make carnitine, which is involved in lipid metabolism and helps the body turn fat into energy.

- The medical research on goji is very limited. A handful of studies found possible benefits that included a feeling of calmness, increased athletic performance, and enhanced quality of sleep. There is also research being conducted that explores the effects that goji berries have in relation to preventing neuronal death in neurodegenerative diseases.

Chocolate

- Another food that was used in ancient Aztec medicine is chocolate. Some believe that the Aztecs thought chocolate was a gift from the gods. It's mentioned in the famous text the *Florentine Codex*, which was an ethnographic text written by a Spanish Franciscan friar, Bernardino de Sahagún. It listed many medical uses for chocolate, including increased libido, fertility assistance, soothing burns, disinfecting cuts, and even facilitating childbirth.

- When chocolate finally reached Europe in the 1600s, it Has introduced as a food and a medicine. In 1631, a Spanish physician, Antonio Colmenero de Ledesma, conducted research and decided that chocolate was, indeed, a medicine. he, along with other medical practitioners, believed that it was good for digestion, helped people gain weight, and could potentially stimulate the nervous system.

- Elsewhere in Europe, it was thought to also help with depression and hypochondria. Research continued into the 18th century.

- In the 21st century, medical research on the beneficial properties of chocolate is having a renaissance. Recently, scientists began exploring chocolate's power to lower high blood pressure and reduce the risk of cardiovascular disease.

- There is limited data to suggest that chocolate may have some beneficial properties. It's an antioxidant, and some tantalizing data suggests that chocolate consumption can improve brain function.

- Despite the promising data, the NIH warns Americans that if you want to eat chocolate, you are doing so for your taste buds— not your health. They are, however, continuing to fund research studies into the health effects of chocolate.

Hibiscus Tea

- Other foods that are popular in the United States that also show promising results but are not yet backed as supplements by the NIH include hibiscus tea and pomegranate fruit. Both were part of ancient Chinese medical practices and are still used today in TCM.

- Some research has shown that drinking hibiscus tea, made out of the flower, can lower systolic blood pressure. Researchers from Tufts University found that drinking 3 cups of herbal tea a day has similar effects as standard prescription blood pressure drugs. The NIH warns that these results must not be taken as definitive evidence. More research is needed.

Pomegranate Fruit

- The pomegranate has a long and rich history all over the world. It was historically seen as a sign of fertility in many places, including the Middle East. It holds religious significance for people of the Jewish faith.

- Research on the health effects of the consumption of all parts of the fruit have been undertaken. This includes not only the fruit and seeds but also the seed oil, peel, root, leaves, and flower. Scientists are interested in the fruit because it's rich in antioxidant tannins and flavonoids.

- While there is not a lot of strong evidence of the beneficial properties of pomegranate, there are clinical trials that suggest that it may help ward off infections.

- Data from a handful of population studies also suggests that eating pomegranate might lower blood pressure, improve signs of heart disease, control dental plaque, and even help fight some cancer growth. But none of this is definitive evidence.

Fish Oil

- Fish oil is either consumed when eating certain fish or as a supplement. Fish oil is very rich in omega-3 fatty acids, which are known to be critical for brain health.

- Many anthropologists believe that our ancestors targeted marine resources, such as fish and shellfish, and that this is part of what allowed our brains to expand. Some claim that early humans' ability to target fish and shellfish may have been the key to our survival during lean times or during population bottlenecks.

- There is research to suggest that omega-3 fatty acids are very good for us. Some evidence suggests that including fish, or fish oil supplements, can be an important part of a heart-healthy diet.

- Other research has explored whether fish oil is helpful in relieving symptoms of rheumatoid arthritis. The data show modest support for this effect. Other research areas that are currently under investigation include the effect that fish oil might have on mental illness, autism, multiple sclerosis, macular degeneration, and even cancer.

Suggested Reading

McKenna, *Food of the Gods*.
Taylor, ed., *Turmeric*.

Questions

1. In his discussion of humoral medicine, what did Hippocrates mean when he stated, "Let food be thy medicine and medicine be thy food"?

2. How are clinical trials used by the Food and Drug Administration and the National Institutes of Health to determine whether a food can also be used as an effective medicine?

LECTURE
25

THE COEVOLUTION
OF GENES AND DIET

Food nourishes us. It is a part of our identity and history, and it has evolved with us. Biology and culture, rather than acting in isolation, have interacted throughout human evolution to develop the diet that we consume today. In this lecture, you will explore the ways in which our genes and diet have coevolved.

Lactose

- Lactose intolerance is when your body cannot digest lactose, the main sugar in milk, very well in adulthood. Compounds in food are sources of energy for cells in the body, but before they can do their job, they have to be broken down into simple molecules that can be absorbed and used by cells.

- Lactose intolerance is caused by a shortage of lactase enzymes, which work to break down lactose into simpler forms of glucose and galactose. Symptoms of lactose intolerance can include cramps, bloating, and other kinds of gastrointestinal distress.

- Lactose intolerance is primarily associated with adulthood because nearly all infants and young children have the lactase enzymes that allow them to digest lactose. We lose our lactase enzymes after weaning. Very rarely, an infant may be born with lactose intolerance, but this is not common and is distinct from the lactose intolerance that affects older children, adolescents, and adults.

- The chances that you might be lactose intolerant vary depending on your ethnic group and its history of using dairy products in the diet. We know that the ability to digest lactase disappears after weaning for most mammals, including us. Despite this, some human populations have developed the ability to digest lactose into adulthood, but this makes up only 1/3 of the world's population.

- Scholars who study milk believe that this genetic change occurred when people began to milk newly domesticated animals, such as cows, goats, and sheep. As people began introducing milk and other dairy products into their diet, mutations near the gene that produces the lactase enzyme also started popping up and becoming more common.

- This means that populations who have a long and sustained evolutionary relationship with dairy products are less likely to be lactose intolerant. People who appear to be lactose tolerant, by and large, are people with a northern European ancestry and those who are from some parts of Africa or Mongolia.

- It turns out that most adults in the world cannot tolerate lactose. The highest prevalence of intolerance is found among Asians, American Indians, Latinos, African Americans, and Ashkenazi Jewish people.

- New research has found that we didn't just automatically begin to tolerate lactose. The Stone Age ancestors of Europeans—the ones who have a long and sustained relationship with dairy—could not digest milk right away.

- Researchers in fields ranging from archaeology, to genetics, to animal husbandry and cattle genetics are interested in how this trait evolved. The combined data suggests that populations in the Middle East and North Africa first domesticated cattle roughly around 7500 or 8000 years ago.

- These cattle were then brought to Europe, where the same advantages of the persistence of the lactase enzyme would be conferred on cattle farmers in those environments.

- In a cattle-friendly, dairy-friendly environment, being able to drink milk would have provided distinct benefits, such as a clean source of hydration during times of drought as well as additional calories.

- We now know that cattle were likely domesticated independently in several places, including Africa. And recent work by genetics and genomics researchers suggest that just as in Europe, mutations randomly arose in Africa that effectively kept the lactase gene switched on in these ethnic groups as well.

- While the lactose tolerance mutation arose randomly, as all genetic mutations do, it had an advantage within these populations and stuck around. Individuals carrying this particular genetic mutation would have been favored by natural selection – and then subsequently spread it to Europe and beyond.

Amylase

- All vertebrates have amylase, an enzyme that is made in the pancreas and secreted into the small intestine. Some mammals—including humans and other primates, rabbits, rodents, and a few bat species—also produce amylase in their saliva. For humans, it helps us digest carbohydrates by breaking down starch to sugar and begins the chemical process of digestion.

- AMY-1 is the name of the gene responsible for producing amylase, and this gene shows high copy-number variability, which means that sections of the human genome are repeated and the number of repeats in the genome can vary between individuals.

- George Perry, director of the Anthropological Genomics Laboratory at Pennsylvania State University, and his colleagues successfully demonstrated with their research that the number of AMY-1 copies in individual genomes corresponded with amylase protein levels in the saliva and that populations with high-starch diets have, on average, more copies than their counterparts with low-starch diets.

- This means that people who produce more salivary amylase are better able to digest starch and are, therefore, maybe able to obtain more energy from starches than people with less amylase.

In an evolutionary context, this makes sense; we know that our ancestors have been targeting starchy potato-like tubers for the better part of 2 million years.

Omega-3 Fatty Acids

- There is also evidence to suggest that there are unique genetic adaptations for metabolizing omega-3 fatty acids, which are beneficial to your brain health and function (and possibly even protective against heart disease), and other fatty acids.

- Most of the medical research that has been done testing the protective effects of omega-3 fatty acids against heart disease or strokes are inconclusive. Evidence suggests that they do lower blood pressure in people with hypertension.

- Based on this, the American Heart Association (AHA) recommends that people who are at high risk for developing cardiovascular disease might want to take omega-3 supplements. For people who are not at high risk, the AHA still recommends eating fish or oils high in these fatty acids a few times a week.

- It looks like a diet high in omega-3 fatty acids might not be as beneficial for all populations, but it turns out that it might still be the case for the Inuit, indigenous peoples from Greenland who live in an arctic environment.

- Greenland has an incredibly lucrative fishing industry. Access to such vast amounts of marine resources is why the Inuit diet contains so many omega-3 polyunsaturated fatty acids.

- In 2015, a large international group of scientists found that the Greenlandic Inuit show genetic signatures of being adapted to both their climate and their diet. They found genetic variants in fat metabolism that allow Inuits to more effectively handle such large doses of polyunsaturated fatty acids in their diet.

- These variations occurred in a cluster of genes that are responsible for the construction of enzymes called fatty acid desaturases. The genes under selection for this dietary adaptation, however, also have a strong effect on height and weight—as well as a protective effect on cholesterol triglyceride levels.

- Geneticist Rasmus Nielsen, one of the senior scientists on the project, argues that these data are critical to increasing our understanding of the ways in which diet can influence evolution. He hypothesizes that the adaptation might be as old as 20,000 years ago, when ancestors of the current-day Inuit were occupying a region known as Beringia, or the Bering Land Bridge.

Nutrigenomics

- The field of nutrigenomics specifically looks at the ways in which diet alters the expression of genetic information. Fascinating data is emerging from this field.

- For example, researchers at the Norwegian University of Science and Technology analyzed the differences in gene expression when comparing people eating different diets. Gene expression is the process by which information from a DNA sequence is used to synthesize gene products, such as proteins.

- The researchers found that a diet of about 65% carbohydrates caused certain classes of genes to, "work overtime." These were genes that affected inflammation in the body as well as the development of cardiovascular disease, some cancers, and type 2 diabetes.

- Phenylketonuria is another representation of the link between genes and diet. Phenylketonuria is an inherited disorder where phenylalanine, an amino acid that is in foods that are high in protein—such as meat, fish, dairy products, and nuts—builds up in the body.

- It builds up because people with PKU don't produce the necessary enzyme to break it down. When too much of it builds up, it can lead to dangerous health problems, such as disordered neural development or even seizures. Therefore, people with PKU have to eat a diet that contains foods that are low in phenylalanine.

- Another fascinating example of nutrigenomics has to do with our ability to taste certain flavors. You may have seen maps that show how different regions of the tongue are responsible for identifying different tastes. The old idea was that the tongue had regions for tastes such as bitter, salty, sweet, sour, and—more recently—umami.

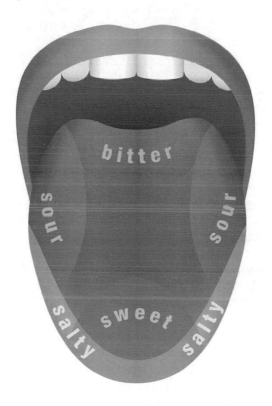

- Data from several different experiments, dating from the 1970s to now, indicate that our tongue is sensitive to all tastes. Our so-called taste buds also extend to our soft palate (the roof of our mouth) and our throats.

- We now know that a wide variety of things contribute to taste. The first factor is the way that we imagine a food tasting; the look and feel of a food contributes to how tasty we think it will be. Our eyes send messages to our brain. Taste, then, according to our brain, is actually a synthesis of a food's taste, smell, and touch combined in a single sensation.

- The other contributing factor to taste is genetics. A certain group of people are dubbed "supertasters," meaning that they can taste flavors more strongly than others.

- Bitter-taste perception is a particularly interesting example that illustrates this phenomenon and the relationship between genes and diet.

- There are 30 genes that are responsible for bitter-taste perception. Different variations of these genes affect the ability to taste bitter compounds in food. Some foods, such as broccoli and Brussels sprouts, taste intolerably bitter to some people—whereas others can't taste them at all.

- The historic argument for why some people have this ability and others don't was that the gene helps us avoid plant toxins that may be harmful. While this explanation was longstanding in the scientific literature, geneticist Sarah Tishkoff set out to determine if this was really the case.

- She tested reactions to glucosinolates, natural components of many plants, including cruciferous vegetables such as broccoli, cauliflower, and Brussels sprouts. Tishkoff's colleagues at the Monell Chemical Senses Center in Philadelphia, Mari Sandell and Paul Breslin, had already begun this work in the early 2000s, when they gave participants vegetables containing high amounts of glucosinolates.

- The participants took a bite of the raw foods, chewed it 10 times to the beat of a metronome, and then spit it out and washed their mouth.

- The researchers also took cheek swabs of the participants to check their DNA—to determine if they had 0, 1, or 2 copies of the bitter-taste receptor gene that would allow them to taste a bitter chemical called phenylthiocarbamide (PTC).

- Their findings showed that a person's genes determine whether they think vegetables are delicious or bitter.

- When Tishkoff teamed up with these researchers, as well as scientists from the National Institutes of Health, Rutgers University, and universities in France and Africa, they decided to put the evolutionary significance of bitter-taste receptors to the test.

- For this experiment, they did not give actual vegetables containing PTC to subjects, but instead spiked their water with it. They found that, globally, the sensitivity to bitterness varied more than they expected.

- Tishkoff and colleagues concluded that perhaps the variation in bitter-taste receptors was linked to something other than bitter taste. Because we have taste genes that are active in our guts and lungs, the idea is that maybe the gene that this team studied has some other, yet unknown, job in those regions.

- Perhaps, then, non-PTC tasters might be better able to taste another substance that also might have provided a survival advantage during our evolutionary past.

Suggested Reading

Cochran and Harpending, *The 10,000 Year Explosion*.
McQuaid, *Tasty*.

Questions

1. How is lactose intolerance an example of gene-culture coevolution?

2. What is the link between genetics and taste receptors?

LECTURE
26

THE SCOOP ON POOP

When studying nutrition, we often think about what we eat, why we eat it, and what eating a particular food might do to our body. But we can also learn a lot by studying the end point of nutrition: poop. This lecture will trace the science and history of excrement from archaeology to nutrition to microbiology.

Fossil Feces

- The oldest poop that has been found is in the form of coprolites, or fossil feces. The world's largest coprolite is thought to come from an unknown reptilian creature living between the Miocene and the Oligocene eras, approximately 20 million years ago. The specimen is 40 inches in length and was sold at an auction in Beverly Hills, California, for about $5000. Coprolites are very popular among fossil collectors.

- There is also a long history of coprolite mining. In the mid- to late 1800s in England, for example, coprolite digging was quite a common practice. Fossilized dung is a good source of phosphate after you treat the substance with sulphuric acid. It could then be used for fertilizer.

- The East of England became a fertilizer hub. England was the site of a coprolite mining rush. One of the reasons for this is because coprolites were one of the cheapest forms of fertilizer. When a farmer ordered it, the coprolite fertilizer would come as a loose powder. It could then be mixed with manure or used on its own.

- Beyond the value as a fertilizer, or the intrigue of purchasing fossil excrement as objects of curiosity, coprolites are also quite valuable to economies. In addition, they're valuable to scientists because they can tell us quite a bit about the diet, ecology, and feeding behavior of animals.

- A great example of the value of coprolites comes from a 77-million-year-old sample from Wyoming. Based on the size and shape of the coprolite—and the context of surrounding material, such as bones and eggshells—scientists were able to determine that this fossil dung came from a dinosaur called the Maiasaura.

- Paleontologist Karen Chin tells us that this species was a 3-ton 9-meter-long herbivore who walked upright on its hind legs. She argues that finding coprolites from ancient plant-eating dinosaurs is critical to understanding past behavior. For example, the Maiasaura ate wood—something that paleontologists never would have expected but that the poop revealed during analysis.

- Other items that have been found in coprolites of various dinosaur species include fossilized bone, teeth, fur, insects, larvae, fish scales, shells, plant seeds, stems, pollen, and fungus.

- Scientists have also used the study of coprolites to inform our understanding of human evolution and human history. Archaeologists working in southern Spain, at a site called El Salt, have uncovered some of the oldest-known human feces to date. These coprolites, which date to around 50,000 years ago, represent some of the oldest human fecal residues that scientists have found.

- There seems to be consensus that these coprolites are Neanderthal. What makes these fecal remains so important to anthropology and researchers interested in the Paleo diet is that they reflect a truly omnivorous diet.

- Many scientists believed for decades that Neanderthals ate a heavily meat-based diet. The common conception was that Neanderthals spent the majority of their time focusing their food-collection efforts on game meat.

- Data from their excrement tells a different story, and it's one that aligns with data collected from other lines of evidence: mainly that Neanderthals, like all of our human ancestors, had a diet that was composed of both plants and animals.

Latrines

- The study of latrines can reveal quite a bit about human history in a variety of contexts. A recent analysis of the sanitation system in ancient Rome yielded some surprising results.

- The Roman Empire is often associated with advances in sanitation, from bathhouses to public toilets and from multi-seat latrines to the waste-removal system that they created to pump human waste out of city and into the countryside.

- But despite these advances, biological anthropologist Piers Mitchell found that ancient Romans were rife with intestinal parasites. Studying the latrine soil and coprolites that were found at several sites, Dr. Mitchell came to the conclusion that despite serious advances in sanitation during the Roman Empire, the Romans don't appear to be any healthier than their Iron Age or Bronze Age counterparts.

- If the presence of toilets and a sanitation system is argued to reduce disease transmission, then how were Romans not healthier than those living in less sanitary conditions? It turns out that water might have been the culprit.

- The warm water in bathhouses was unlikely to be changed very often, leading to a proliferation of bacteria. A layer of scum on the top of water would also make a great home to parasites such as whipworms, tapeworms, and roundworms. In addition to water, historians tell us that ancient Romans were also probably eating bacteria.

- Roman farmers often used human feces as a fertilizer, which was indeed effective for growing crops. However, no one knew about bacteria in those days, and the farmers did not realize that the fertilizer might infect the population who was eating the unwashed produce or produce washed in water hosting its own colony of parasites.

- In addition, the ancient Romans were very fond of *garum*, an uncooked and fermented fish sauce. Eating these fish, or their organs, uncooked and fermented likely led to very high parasite loads in the consumers

Stool Composition

- We can learn a lot about our own health by looking to the end product of our digestion. Because it can often tell you quite a bit about disease and infection, it's important to know your poop.

Specifically, it's important to get to know the signs of a healthy bowel movement.

- Bowel movements are our bodies' natural way of eliminating waste. They tend to be brown in color. Any abnormal changes in color can be a red flag that you may not be healthy.

- Gastroenterologists often caution that black is a color that likely indicates bleeding in the upper gastrointestinal tract. The ingestion of other items might also cause a black color, such as some antidiarrheal medications or iron supplements, so it's not always an indicator of a health problem.

- Red stools, which may also be a health concern, might be caused by problems in the lower gastrointestinal tract, such as hemorrhoids, or, in severe cases, cancer. The red hue might also be caused from eating cranberries, tomato juice, or too many beets.

- If your stool is green, this might be due to eating leafy greens or green food coloring, or it might be the sign of something more serious. It may be due to food moving through your large intestine too quickly, which means that the bile doesn't have time to completely break down, thus causing a green color.

- Mayo Clinic states that there are other colors that you might also want to watch out for—anything that isn't your standard brown— and urges people to look before they flush to evaluate shape, color, and consistency.

- The shape of your stool is another indicator of health. Doctors used to think that the only shape you had to worry about was a pencil-thin one, which may be an indicator of rectal cancer. Now doctors are saying that size and shape might be irrelevant and that human variation is normal.

- Many doctors urge you to be aware of whether your stool floats. If it does, it might indicate malabsorption, meaning that your body might not be absorbing enough fats from the food that you're eating. This is common with celiac disease or pancreatitis.

Fiber and Flatulence

- Some doctors urge people to eat fiber to make sure that their stool is the right size and shape. Fiber acts as a stool-bulking agent, which most nutritionists and health professionals believe is beneficial to your digestive health.

- Some anthropologists, however, have alternative ideas on fiber that are sometimes counter to what nutritionists believe. This is because, from an evolutionary standpoint, fiber is not always a net positive to human consumers. It can be very difficult to digest, reduce the energetic value of food, speed intestinal transit times that limit digestive enzyme activity, and can inhibit absorption of micronutrients, particularly minerals.

- We often hear about 2 types of fiber: soluble and insoluble. Soluble fiber can dissolve in water. It is in nuts, beans, lentils, and blueberries. Insoluble fiber does not dissolve in water, but it can help move food through your digestive system, which can promote regularity and prevent constipation. Foods containing insoluble fiber include whole wheat, legumes, couscous, and cucumber skins.

- Most fiber escapes digestion in the small intestine and is passed into the large intestine, or colon. Until quite recently, most health professionals only talked about fiber as soluble versus insoluble. This is changing, however, as we learn more about the bacteria that reside in our digestive systems.

- Some types of dietary fiber that pass into the large intestine are fermented by gut bacteria that resides in our colon that then produces metabolites, such as short-chain fatty acids, that recycle energy back to the human body.

- The role of fiber in our digestion and how it's linked to the colonies of bacteria in our digestive system is an ongoing line of research.

- The bacteria in our guts plays a big role in the health of our bowel movements. The trillions of little bugs that swim around in our gastrointestinal tract not only influence our digestive and metabolic processes but also influence the smell of excrement.

- The way that your stool smells can indicate health problems, and doctors urge people to take notice of anything out of the ordinary. The bacteria that live in our gut cause the odor, and the fact that it has an unpleasant aroma is a good sign that your resident bacterial freeloaders are doing their job to keep your digestive system healthy.

- It's a similar situation when considering flatulence. When your body is digesting your food, gut bacteria are feasting on the proteins in the food that contain sulfur. This generates gases, such as methanethiol, which, when they escape your body, can smell.

- Passing gas is indicative of a healthy immune system, according to gastroenterologists. This can happen when foods are not absorbed sufficiently into our intestines, so particles sit in our gut and ferment.

Transit Time and Regularity

- By looking at transit time, which is the amount of time that it takes for food to move through your digestive tract, we can learn a lot about diet. While some argue that a fast transit time is preferred, one that is too fast or too long may indicate that the nutrients in your food are not absorbing. Scientists argue that the best transit time is between 12 to 24 hours after consumption.

- In addition to transit time, researchers and medical health professionals are often also concerned with the regularity of bowel movements. One of the most interesting aspects of regularity is that the concept of normal is relative. Because so much of our stool content has to do with diet, the amount of fiber that you eat can dictate how often you have to go.

- Vegetarians, for example, who tend to have diets that are high in fiber, have faster transit times than people consuming more meat.

- Other concerns about transit time include a speeding up of the process, or a slowing down. Diarrhea, which might be caused by a bad meal or harmful bacteria, is a result of your stool passing too quickly through the large intestine, where most of the water content is absorbed.

- Constipation, on the other hand, could be a result of not enough fiber in your diet, changes in physical activity and exertion, or dehydration. Some studies have suggested that if you are constipated, sitting on the throne for an extended period of time is actually a bad idea. The longer you sit, the more likely you are to develop swollen blood vessels, which can lead to hemorrhoids.

- There is some research to suggest that position matters. Squatting is often thought to be beneficial, as greater hip flexion means less strain. There are several footstools on the market that mimic squatting.

- The most common answer to swollen blood vessels, however, is to increase fiber intake. Doctors agree that taking fiber may be one of the best ways to combat constipation.

- Fiber might also be beneficial to your bowel movements in additional ways. Scientists now argue that the bacteria in our gut are fiber-famished. The beneficial bacterial species that we need in our digestive system can be maintained by a diet high in fiber.

Suggested Reading

Waltner-Toews, David. *The Origin of Feces*.

Questions

1. What are coprolites, and how do they inform our understanding of past diets?

2. What is the most accepted definition of dietary fiber, and what role does it play in our digestion?

LECTURE
27

THE GUT MICROBIOME

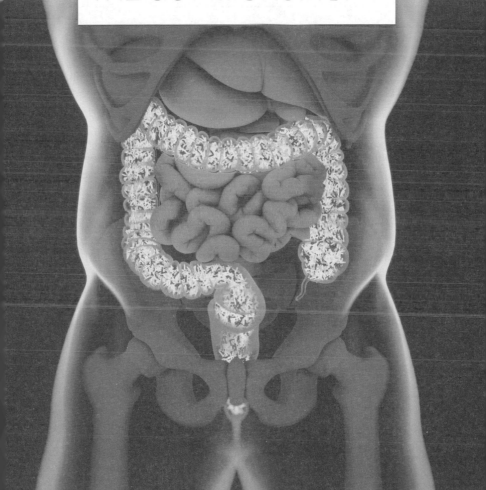

The study of the human microbiome is one of the new frontiers in scientific research. The human microbiome is the full collection of the genes of microbes and microorganisms, and it can be considered the bacterial counterpart to the human genome. Microbes are microscopic organisms that live in or on our bodies. The term "microbiota" describes the total of all of these organisms. This lecture explains why the microbiome is important, paying special attention to the gut microbiome.

Our Microbiome

- The exploration of the diverse communities that reside within our body are not new—only the sophistication of the methods used to analyze them are. Investigations of oral and fecal microbiota started with Antonie van Leeuwenhoek in the 1680s.

- Often called the father of microbiology, van Leeuwenhoek is probably most well known for his improvement of the microscope. He is credited with inventing hundreds of different types of single-lens microscopes and more than 500 optical lenses. He's also credited with being the first person to identify microbiota.

- The microbial communities that reside within us are strikingly different from the free-living microbial communities that exist outside of our bodies. Our epithelial surfaces come into contact with the outside world and, in doing so, come into contact with exogenous bacteria and microorganisms—not to mention viruses. They are the first contact between our body and what is external to our body. Given this constant contact, an individual's microbiome changes throughout his or her lifetime, from in utero to death.

- The microbiomes of various parts of our bodies—such as our eyes, mouths, ears, hands, feet, and genitals—are not only vastly different from each other but are also vastly different from one person to another.

The Gut Microbiome

- Of all of the body's microbiomes, the gut microbiome has the greatest number of bacterial species compared to any other area of the human body. Our gut microbiota play a vital role in our overall health. They are incredibly important for the metabolism of both food and drugs, and they protect against pathogens.

- Our gut flora play a role how our bodies metabolize nutrients, how our bodies store fat, how we balance blood glucose levels, and how we respond to hormones that make us feel either hungry or satiated. The microbiota living in our guts get most of their nutrition from dietary carbohydrates—food that we eat that works, in turn, to feed the colonies of bacteria that we host.

- The carbohydrates that escape digestion, such as dietary fiber, are fermented by organisms in our colons, which results in the synthesis of short-chain fatty acids, which are sources of energy for us—the host.

- Our gut microbiota also play an important role in breaking down various polyphenols that we consume in our diet. Polyphenols are plant compounds that are thought to have antioxidant properties. While they are typically inactive in diet, after the gut flora have removed the sugar molecules of the food we eat, they are transformed to active compounds that can be absorbed and successfully travel to other tissues and organs in the body, providing antimicrobial and metabolic actions.

- Diet is, therefore, critical to shaping not only the composition of the bacteria in our guts but also the diversity and richness of the colonies that we host.

- Starting from infancy, what we eat plays a large role in seeding our gut microbiome. The diet that an infant consumes in early life, either breast milk of formula, can have a cascade effect on the composition of their gut microbiota. Several bioactive compounds are found only in breast milk and cannot be found in formula. These compounds play roles in nutrient digestion and absorption as well as immune protection.

- The first 2 years of a child's life are critical to building the population of commensal bacteria that they will carry around with them. And what we eat throughout our lifetime continues to influence our microbiota.

- The type of lipids and plant-based carbohydrates that we eat dictates the structure of the microbial taxonomic community residing in our guts. The beneficial bacterial species that we need in our digestive system can be maintained by a diet high in fiber, particularly microbiota-accessible carbohydrates, found in fruits, vegetables, whole grains, legumes, and seaweed.

- These exogenous sources of food for our bacteria are called prebiotics; they are the nondigestible parts of our food and help our bacteria flourish.

- Probiotics, on the other hand, are microbial supplements that are consumed for health reasons. You can eat probiotic foods, such as fermented sauerkraut or kombucha, or you can take probiotic supplements in pill form. They can help increase the diversity of your microbiota and/or help move food through your gut.

- The wrong mix of microbes in our gut appears to help set the stage for some diseases. Dysbiosis, or an imbalance of the gut

microbiota, has now been linked with an array of diseases, ranging from Irritable bowel syndrome and Crohn's disease; to metabolic diseases, such as obesity and diabetes; to chronic allergies and even neurodevelopmental illnesses.

- The so-called gut-brain axis is increasingly implicated in schizophrenia, bipolar disorder, autism, and dementia. The gut-brain axis is a regulatory and communicative system involving various structures in the body, including the brain, central nervous system, and gut.

- Because this system is bidirectional, it means that the brain and the gut both send and receive messages. This is done through the enteric nervous system, which is a system of neurons that governs the function of our gastrointestinal systems.

- The gut, and all of its microbial residents, therefore directly influence things like immunity, endocrine function, and the nervous system. They also aid in the regulation of behavior.

- While this particular line of research is still in its infancy and the strength of evidence is not as robust as many scientists would like it to be, there is great interest in this field, and many research hours and dollars are being spent trying to better understand these causal links.

- One fruitful line of inquiry has been exploring the ways in which bacterial genes have hitchhiked into our genome. Scientists at the University of Cambridge have recently discovered that almost 150 of the genes in human genome are bacterial genes that have jumped into human DNA over the course of our evolution in a process called horizontal gene transfer.

- This process is discussed very often today in regard to antibiotic use. The normal, healthy human gut microbiome is altered over the long term when antibiotics are repeatedly used. The horizontal transfer of antibiotic-resistance genes could potentially result in an assembly of flora with a multidrug-resistant gene pool. This is why, increasingly, there is a move away from the routine use of broad-spectrum antibiotics.

- The evolutionary implications of such work are astounding and lead us to what scientists call the old friends hypothesis, originally proposed in the early 2000s by Professor Graham Rook. The hypothesis proposes that vital microbes have been present throughout human evolution and that, as a result, our immune system is dependent on certain strains that evolved with the human species.

- Rook's hypothesis suggests that because people and their microbes depend on each other to function properly, their absence might cause abnormal functioning of the immune system.

- Our ancestors evolved with microbial communities, coming into close and sustained contact with the environment around them. More than 95% of human evolution has taken place in the context of a hunter-gatherer lifestyle, in outdoor environments with repeated exposure to soil, water, vegetation, and animal products.

- To more fully explore this hypothesis, researchers have begun to look to small-scale societies who live in conditions as similar as possible to the environments in which we evolved. Until very recently, most research has focused on postindustrialized Western populations, whose microbiome is likely to be quite different from populations who live in urban environments.

- While the Hadza foragers of Tanzania are by no means a fossil population, they live in an environment and practice a lifestyle that is the closest approximation that we can measure to that of our ancestors. Alyssa Crittenden and colleagues undertook an ambitious research project that aimed at characterizing the Hadza gut microbiome. It was the first study of its kind, and it yielded important and interesting results.

- Results showed that the Hadza have an entirely unique configuration of bacteria in their guts, unlike any population previously sampled. They have a much more diverse microbe ecosystem, with more species of gut bacteria than populations from postindustrialized settings. The Hadza experience little-to-no autoimmune diseases that typically result from gut-bacteria imbalances.

- Gleaning information about their microbiome is critical to understanding the old friends hypothesis and how our gut microbiota in a Western urban environment are different.

- The Hadza showed evidence of antibiotic-resistance genes. This is interesting, because they were a population with limited to no exposure to antibiotics at the time of data collection. These results suggest that the Hadza have environmentally derived resistances.

- The take-home messages are that diversity is key—the more bacterial species, the better—and that our microbial partners are external means of both functional activity and evolutionary selection. The data supports the idea that these microbes certainly are fellow travelers in human evolution.

- Hunter-gatherers subsist on wild foods and face both seasonal and annual fluctuations in resource availability. They consume food that exposes them to beneficial microbes, which then influence the composition of their gut microbiome.

- People living in urban environments, on the other hand, subsist on industrialized foods and do not face the same type of seasonal restrictions on availability. We consume food that has been processed and often commercially washed and prepared. We use sterile cleaners that promise consumers that they kill 99% of germs and bacteria. Even our soaps are antibacterial. And many of us have also had several rounds of antibiotics throughout our lifetime.

- All of this adds up to create a microbiome that is quite different from people in rural settings—and from the environment in which we evolved.

Antibiotics

- Humans have long used bacteria to fight infection. We have known since the 19th century that specific types of bacteria cause disease. Based on this discovery, we made moves to increase sanitation and hygiene, such as introducing routine garbage collection and potable water, which led to drastic reductions of infectious diseases.

- The first true antibiotic, penicillin, was discovered in 1928 by Alexander Fleming. The widespread introduction of penicillin happened in the 1940s, and the age of antibiotics began.

- The use of antibiotics has been considered one of the greatest advances in medicine, controlling the spread of infectious diseases that were the leading causes of human mortality for most of human existence.

- While we worked to wipe out the "bad" bacteria, we inadvertently wiped out the "good" bacteria as well. The first scientist to specifically acknowledge that some germs are good for us was British epidemiologist David Strachan. In the late 1980s, he proposed the hygiene hypothesis, which argued that exposure to infections during childhood may provide defense against allergies later in life.

- Strachan argued that a lack of exposure to some infectious agents and parasites would increase susceptibility to allergic diseases because the natural development of the immune system would be suppressed.

- This hypothesis—also known as the biome depletion hypothesis or the lost friends hypothesis—has had amazing traction with the medical community. We now know that this idea applies to a much broader range of diseases, such as irritable bowel syndrome, Crohn's disease, and even multiple sclerosis.

- Many medical researchers now suggest that the best way forward is to combine several strategies of increasing our microbial load.

- Most preventative measures encourage parents to start early in life, with natural childbirth and breastfeeding. Other parental behaviors during infancy include not washing a baby's pacifier when it hits the floor. Another thing that appears to help young children build a strong and beneficial microbial community is having a pet.

- Other recommendations include spending more time exercising. Researchers also urge people to spend more time outside, which can increase the diversity of your microbiome.

- The most common advice to tend your bacterial colony is to avoid the use of hand sanitizer, sterilizing cleaning products, and antibiotics and to eat your way to a healthier microbiome.

- Roughage is not only good for you—the host—but it's also good for your resident microbes. Fermented treats, such as kimchi, sauerkraut, and kombucha, encourage the growth of good bacteria. You can also eat more foods that contain microbiota-accessible carbohydrates, such as artichokes, garlic, asparagus, beans, whole grains, and legumes.

Suggested Reading

Ingraham, *Kin.*
Waltner-Toews, David. *The Origin of Feces.*

Questions

1. What are microbiota, and how can they inform our understanding of gut health and function?

2. How does the old friends hypothesis inform our understanding of human evolution and the immune system?

LECTURE
28

BRAIN FOOD

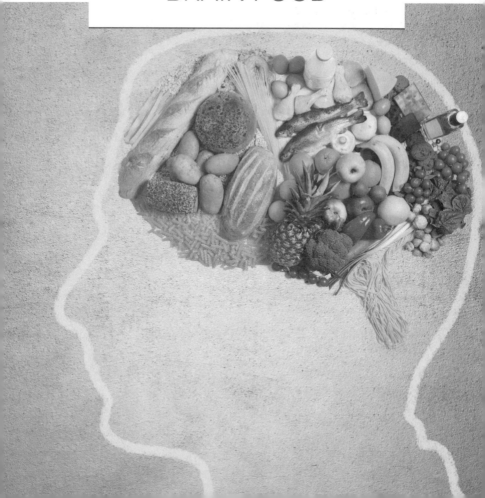

Diet and the brain are inextricably linked. They have been entwined from the beginning, during our evolutionary past as well as in our cultural and biological present. This lecture will explore the links between our brains and our diet from many different perspectives. Our appreciation of these links will only grow as we learn more about how diet affects mood, weight, addiction, and even cognitive performance.

The Human Brain and Diet

- During the evolution of our genus, *Homo*, brain size dramatically increased. But it's not only about absolute size. The thing to pay attention to is something called the encephalization quotient, which is the ratio between actual brain size and predicted brain size based on an animal's body size. While many animals have much larger brains than ours, it's how big our brain is compared to our body that makes us unique.

- Whether the ancestral diet was mostly meat or mostly plants is still up for debate. A group of scientists, mostly anthropologists and archaeologists, stress the importance of marine and freshwater resources in our evolutionary past.

- Fish and fish oil are wonderful sources of omega-3 fatty acids. Docosahexaenoic acid and icosapentaenoic acid are 2 omega-3 fatty acids that evolutionary biologists are particularly interested in. They are critical for brain health during development and in adulthood.

- When early members of our genus switched to high-quality foods, whatever those may have been, it gave our brains the energy that they needed to expand. Many researchers think that it was the incredible diversity of foods in the panoply of the early human diet that made all the difference. The relationship between our brains and our guts has been a hallmark of our evolution.

- Only about 2/3 of our brain's energy is being used to help nerve cells or neurons send signals. The rest of it is being used for basic cell-health maintenance, so it's important to feed our brain the energy that it needs to properly function.

- The brain is also a metabolically expensive organ. While it's only about 2% of your body's weight, it consumes about 20% of your oxygen and gets about 20% of your blood flow.

- Energy travels to our brains via blood vessels in the form of glucose, which we get from food. Glucose is then transported across the blood-brain barrier and produces adenosine triphosphate, which transports energy within cells for metabolism.

- Your brain is in regular communication with your gut. There are about 100 million neurons that line your digestive system and stay in communication with your brain via your vagus nerve, which is the longest of the 12 cranial nerves. It reaches from your brainstem to the lowest part of your abdomen and touches most major organs along the way, including the heart, lungs, and esophagus.

- The vagus nerve sends sensory information about the body to the brain—and from the brain to the body. Our gut instincts get transferred up to our brains via the vagus nerve. The sensory information that the vagus nerve sends to the brain has been linked to moderating mood and some types of fear and anxiety.

- The relatively new field of nutritional psychiatry explores the link between diet and mental health. Promising data from different age groups and cultures suggests that dietary improvement can also lead to improvement in mood.

- Another way in which your stomach is linked to your behavior is when blood is diverted from other areas and supplied to the stomach, such as after a big meal to digest all of the food that you just ate. This can make you feel sleepy.

- Some link the sleepy feeling after eating turkey to tryptophan, which is an amino acid that makes serotonin, which can make you feel calm, relaxed, and tired. Therefore, it isn't actually the tryptophan in your turkey that makes you sleepy after the big meal—it's that you have overeaten.

- Other foods that we commonly eat at big holiday meals, such as creamy and buttery mashed potatoes or pie, are high in glucose. They have what is called a high glycemic index, which is a value that is assigned to foods and is based on how quickly or slowly the food in question increases blood sugar, or blood glucose levels.

- Foods that are low on the glycemic index scale release glucose at a slow and steady output. Foods that are high on the index, on the other hand, release glucose quickly.

- High-glycemic-index foods can assist with energy recovery linked with hypoglycemia (low blood sugar) or after a workout. Low-glycemic index foods are often said to aid in weight loss and are suggested for people with diabetes.

- For diabetics, a low-glycemic-index diet can be quite beneficial. Diabetics are unable to produce sufficient amounts of insulin and have an excess of blood glucose, so low-glycemic-index foods are helpful in keeping blood glucose under control, as the glucose is released at a slow and steady rate.

- Insulin is a hormone that is made in the pancreas that allows our body to use the glucose from the foods we eat. The more you eat, the more insulin is released, as a normal part of the digestive process. The insulin, then, increases the production of other compounds, such as serotonin.

- Serotonin can affect mood and make you feel calm. It has also been said to influence social behavior, sleep patterns, memory, and even sexual desire. Remarkably, most of the body's serotonin, somewhere around 80% to 90%, can be found in the gastrointestinal tract. It's this link between serotonin and our gut that might be responsible for the urge to snack.

- Leptin is also thought to play a critical role in appetite. It's technically an adipokin, which is essentially a small protein that's important for cell signaling. It is a hormonelike molecule. It is secreted by our fat cells and is responsible for sending the message to our brain that we feel full. Leptin is important for long-term regulation of energy balance by inducing weight loss. It's often called the satiation hormone.

- Since its discovery in 1994, leptin has received a lot attention for its ability to help curb the global obesity pandemic. Research is still under way as we learn more about the ways in which circulating leptin levels affect satiation.

- Ghrelin, on the other hand, is called the hunger hormone. When your stomach is empty, it's secreted. According to a team of researchers led by Dr. Michael Schwartz, ghrelin acts on the brain cells in the hypothalamus to simultaneously increase feelings of hunger and increase secretion of gastric acid and gastrointestinal motility, which essentially prepares the body for the intake of food.

- While the big hormones to consider are insulin, leptin, and ghrelin, other molecules are at work, too. Orexin is one of them. Also called hypocretin, it's a neuropeptide that controls and regulates feelings of wakefulness, sexual arousal, and even appetite.

Food Cravings and Addiction

- There is a lot of research being conducted that explores the link between food cravings and addiction. It has been studied in a number of ways but most commonly under the umbrella of obesity and health-related research.

- Brains sometimes respond to food in the same way that they respond to drugs. Foods such as ice cream and pizza can actually elicit cravings and trigger responses that are similar to those caused by addictive drugs, such as cocaine.

- Certain foods trigger a reward center in the brain. The trick is trying to figure out what is addiction and what is pleasure from the food that we are eating.

- Scientists are particularly interested in binge eating. It turns out that there are certain neural structures, neurochemical profiles, that characterize binge eaters that also characterize drug addicts. While it remains controversial, there is a growing body of medical literature that supports the idea.

- Other similarities between food addicts and drug addicts include abnormalities in the dopamine and opioid neurotransmitter systems. Dopamine is a molecule that tends to be behind many of our cravings, from lust to gambling to food addiction. Dopamine is a neurotransmitter, which means that it's a chemical signal that passes information between neurons.

- Dopamine is able to signal feedback for predicted rewards. For example, if you see a cupcake, your brain might predict the award of consuming that cupcake and you get a flood of dopamine. If you don't eat it, however, then your dopamine levels can decrease, making you feel irritable and sad. Over time, your brain changes and the dopamine receptors are reduced, making those cupcakes less enjoyable—but still craved.

- Many of the drugs used to treat opiate addiction and alcohol dependency can also decrease food consumption, particularly during binges. It must be noted, however, that how dopamine links to food-related addiction is not as well understood as its role in drug addiction, so more research in this area is needed.

- Another added dimension is genetics. It turns out that many people suffering from food dependency have a particular genetic profile that affects dopamine pathways. This means that some people have a greater susceptibility for dysfunction in their neural reward system.

- Research has also shown that cognitive defects, such as increased memory loss, can be linked with food. Diets that are high in saturated fat, for example, are becoming notorious in medical circles for reducing cognitive processing abilities and increasing the risk of neurological dysfunction.

Eating for Your Brain

- The MIND diet—which stands for Mediterranean-DASH Intervention for Neurodegenerative Delay, according to Mayo Clinic—is a diet that nutritiontists and medical practitioners say is for our brain. It is based on the Mediterranean diet and the DASH diet.

- The Mediterranean diet is a heart-healthy diet that is based on foods and cuisine from the Mediterranean. Mayo Clinic enthusiastically recommends this diet and reports that a long-term study of 1.5 million healthy adults demonstrated that the Mediterranean diet is linked to a reduced risk for cardiovascular mortality, cancer, Parkinson's disease, and Alzheimer's disease. They also suggest that women who eat a Mediterranean diet, with added extra-virgin olive oil and mixed nuts, might have reduced risk of contracting breast cancer.

- This diet includes primarily plant-based nutrition supplemented with fish a few times a week and limits red meat consumption to a few times a month. It calls for replacing butter with healthy fats, such as olive oil, and trading in salt for herbs and spices. It also urges people to exercise and to enjoy the occasional glass of red wine.

- The DASH diet, which stands for Dietary Approaches to Stop Hypertension, is designed to help treat or prevent high blood pressure and, according to Mayo Clinic, can help prevent osteoporosis, cancer, heart disease, stroke, and diabetes.

- The DASH diet is low in saturated fat, total fat, and cholesterol and is based on about 2000 calories a day. It includes whole grains, fruits, vegetables, low-fat dairy products, and limited fish, poultry, and legumes. You are encouraged to eat a small number of nuts and seeds a few times a week and limit consumption of red meat, sweets, and fats to very small amounts.

- The MIND diet, which was designed to slow cognitive decline, is a hybrid of these 2 diets. It includes a list of foods that Mayo Clinic says are "brain-healthy," including vegetables of all kinds but particularly green leafy vegetables, nuts and berries, beans and whole grains, and seafood and poultry. They also suggest olive oil and wine.

- Mayo Clinic also classifies foods that it considers to be unhealthy for the brain. These include red meat, butter and margarine, cheese, and sweets and fried foods.

- Some of the foods on the "do eat" list are the usual suspects. For example, we have long known that diets rich in omega-3 fatty acids support cognitive processes. It's one of the many touted benefits of taking fish oil as a supplement. Berries making the list is also not a surprise; they contain antioxidants, including those that are thought to protect against cancer and some types of dementia.

Suggested Reading

Braun, *Buzz*.
Wenk, *Your Brain on Food*.

Questions

1. What is the encephalization quotient, and what does it tell us about the evolution of the human brain?

2. Why are omega-3 fatty acids critical for brain health, and what food sources provide them?

LECTURE
29

YOU ARE WHAT
YOUR MOTHER ATE

What you eat as a pregnant woman affects the baby inside of you. New data even suggests that what you eat before you are pregnant has an effect not only on your child but potentially on your grandchildren, too. In this lecture, you will learn about such intergenerational effects and a fascinating new field of science that is rapidly informing the way we understand how maternal diet influences disease. You will also learn about the types of micronutrients that are important.

Important Micronutrients

- Vitamin B_{12}, also called cobalamin, is one of 8 B vitamins that helps the body produce energy. It is one of the vitamins known as the B complex and helps with neural function and maintaining healthy nerve cells. B_{12} is also important for making red blood cells, which it does in partnership with folic acid, or vitamin B_9, also called folate.

- Because it is a B vitamin, it isn't water soluble, which means that our body doesn't store it. It's eliminated in our urine, so we need to consume it to keep it in our diet. It is found in animal products such as dairy, eggs, meat, fish, and shellfish.

- This means that vegetarians and vegans may be at a higher risk for deficiency. This is one of the reasons that the American Dietetic Association has recommended supplemental vitamin B_{12} for vegetarian and vegan expectant and nursing mothers.

- Some research has reported that low vitamin B_{12} levels during pregnancy can negatively affect mental function in infants and that infants who are breastfed by a mother who is deficient in

B_{12} are at increased risk for anemia, growth failure, and other developmental disorders.

- Adults who are deficient in this vitamin can suffer from brain and nerve damage and, if it gets serious enough, have a higher risk of developing dementia and some forms of psychosis.

- Another vitamin that women are urged to consume during pregnancy is folate or folic acid, both of which are water-soluble B vitamins. Folate is the vitamin that occurs naturally in food, and folic acid is the synthetic form that is often added to supplements. Foods that have folic acid include nuts, beans, green leafy vegetables, and citrus fruits as well as supplements and many fortified foods.

- Women are told that they must get enough folate or folic acid during pregnancy to ensure that their infants have proper neurodevelopment. When a pregnant woman hasn't ingested enough folate during pregnancy, her infant is at greater risk of having neural-tube defects or spina bifida, which is a split or splayed vertebral column.

- The idea is to make sure that you get the optimum amount, which can be difficult for expectant mothers today, as people are eating more processed foods and fewer fresh ones. The United States has laws that require folate to be added to fortified foods to improve the folate status of pregnant women.

- Mothers are also warned that having too much folate or B_{12} in their system can also be bad for the developing fetus, and a combination of high folate levels and low vitamin B_{12} levels might be linked with increased risk of insulin resistance and obesity in their children.

- Research is ongoing, as medical practitioners are trying to determine the best way to ensure that mothers get the optimum amount of the vitamins that they—and their infants—need.

- Most antenatal heath advice urges expectant mothers to take a prenatal vitamin. This ensures that they get adequate amounts of not only folate and B_{12}, but also calcium, vitamin D, iron, and iodine.

- Calcium is important for pregnant women—not only to ensure that her own bone density stays where it needs to be, but it is also important for her infant. A pregnant woman's need for calcium increases during her third trimester, when the fetus is growing its bones. The fetal skeleton will get what it needs to develop, even if this means taking some of the mother's own calcium that she is using for her bone density.

- Vitamin D also plays a role in immune function. Deficiencies in vitamin D have been linked to preeclampsia in pregnant women and other associated negative outcomes in nonpregnant people. These include decreased muscle strength, increased risk of falling, and increased risk for some types of cancer.

- There are 2 ways to get vitamin D: ingest it or expose your skin to it. Dietary sources include dairy, egg yolk, salmon, and cod-liver oil, but most people get their vitamin D from fortified sources, such as milk or supplements. The other way to get vitamin D is through exposure to the Sun, particularly ultraviolet B rays.

- Iron is another important micronutrient for mothers during pregnancy. The World Health Organization has made strong recommendations that women take both folate and iron as part of their daily antenatal care to reduce the risk of anemia and iron deficiency for themselves and low birth weight for their infant.

- Pregnancy is a critical time for iron because a woman's body uses more of it to make extra blood during pregnancy—for her and her fetus. Iron also plays a role in moving oxygen from the lungs to the rest of her body and her infant's.

- Iron comes in 2 forms: heme and nonheme iron. Nonheme iron can be found in plant foods such as rice, wheat, oats, nuts, fruits, vegetables, and supplements. It also makes up about 60% of the iron content of meat. Meat, unlike plants, also contains the other type of iron—heme iron—which makes up the remainder of its iron content.

- Heme iron is easily absorbed by our bodies; nonheme iron is not absorbed as well. Most nutritional guides for pregnancy urge women to eat a diet that is rich in both plant and animal sources of iron.

- Vegetarians and vegans are encouraged to talk to their doctors about finding plant foods that have a high nonheme iron content. Including a dose of vitamin C with your plant-based iron, such as strawberries or orange juice, can help you absorb significantly more iron from beans, for example.

- Iodine is also important for pregnancy. Iodine is necessary for thyroid-hormone production, and deficiencies can result in the development of goiters, neurocognitive impairments, and, in some cases, cretinism.

- According to the World Health Organization, iodine deficiency disorder affects 2 billion people worldwide. Iodine is critical during pregnancy. Not only is it necessary for the healthy functioning of the mother's thyroid, but a deficiency in iodine can lead to miscarriage, stunted physical growth, mental disability, and hearing loss in infants. Table salt is fortified with iodine.

Developmental Programming

- In addition to developmental effects that are a consequence of nutrient deficiencies in maternal diet, there is also something else at play called developmental programming. In this case, developmental has to do with prenatal life, and programming has to do with priming the infant's physiological systems during early development to cope with the nutritional environment—both inside the womb during gestation and in the outside world after.

- The field of developmental programming examines how nongenetic factors, such as a mother's nutritional environment when she is pregnant, can influence genetic variation that has lifelong, and even generational, effects. Research that falls under this domain is done in multiple disciplines, including public health, genetics, clinical practice, evolutionary medicine, and anthropology.

- When a mother is calorie restricted during pregnancy, her developing child responds by adapting to this nutritionally poor environment to survive in a similarly poor nutritional environment outside of the womb.

- When this child's developmentally programmed "thrifty metabolism" encounters a nutritional environment that is not restricted, this often leads to obesity, heart disease, and type 2 diabetes because the metabolism was primed, or programmed, to maximize the nutrition available.

- When there are more calories, fats, and sugars available, the thrifty metabolism turns those extra calories into visceral fat, increased plaque in the arteries, and excessive sugar in the bloodstream.

- This type of diet, coupled with low fiber intake and limited physical activity, is one that characterizes most Americans today—and, increasingly, much of the world. We now have overwhelming evidence to suggest that a fast-food diet and little-to-no exercise are risk factors for developing cardiometabolic diseases in adult life.

- Researchers long thought that the biggest risk factors were familial genetic risk. If you had heart disease in your family, for example, that meant that you were much more likely to inherit those genes and also increase your risk. This is true. But it wasn't until relatively recently that scientists also realized that what your mother, and even grandmother, ate could have negative effects on your adult health.

- In fact, we now know that it extends beyond mothers and grandmothers. The diet of fathers, grandfathers, and other more distant ancestors can also have serious consequences.

- Scientists think that there are a few different ways that this programming might occur. The first one is continued environmental exposure, meaning repeated exposure during critical periods of development, generation after generation.

- Some scientists argue that the reasons that multiple generations suffer from these health conditions is because they all suffered from food insecurity. Given sociopolitical factors, some populations are exposed to more nutrient-restricted conditions over several generations, leading to developmentally programmed traits that contribute to the health disparities we see today.

- The second mechanism is the idea that the maternal uterine environment influences the infant long after gestation and birth. Researchers now believe that there is a direct link between low birth weight and adult risk for diseases such as cardiometabolic syndrome, hypertension, glucose intolerance, and obesity. The way that this happens is through epigenetics.

Epigenetics

- Epigenetics is the study of gene expression, meaning whether a gene is turned on or off. This process of turning genes on and off is called gene regulation. Every cell turns on, or expresses, only a fraction of the genes that it has. The rest of the genes are turned off, or repressed.

- Genes are turned on and off during development, which allows the cells to react, as needed, to changes in their environment.

- Epigenetics is often as important as one's DNA code. One easy way to differentiate genetics versus epigenetics is to think about traditional genetics as the way the DNA sequences in our genes are passed from one generation to the next. Epigenetics, then, describes passing on the way that the genes are used. It's the study of potentially heritable changes in gene expression rather than the gene code itself.

- In the last several decades, research in the field of epigenetics has revolutionized the way that the medical community thinks about the global health patterns that we see today. Much more attention is being paid to the 9 months that infants spend in utero and what this means later in life.

- And it's not just what is happening during pregnancy—what mothers are eating once they know that they gestating. It turns out that what mothers eat in the weeks and months leading up to a pregnancy is also important.

- According to the Epigenome NoE, a European and U.S.-based research consortium, mothers can eat for their epigenome.

  - For folic acid, the consortium suggests eating a healthy serving of beans, leafy vegetables, and maybe some sunflower seeds.

- For choline, the recommendation is to eat eggs, peanuts, and liver (but not in massive quantities).

- For methionine, one of the essential amino acids that's important for the growth of new blood cells, you can eat tofu, spinach, garlic, kidney beans, fish, or eggs.

- For B_{12}, fish is a good source.

- For zinc, oysters are not a bad option, although doctors recommend that pregnant women avoid raw shellfish.

- Resveratrol is a main component of most red wines. It is thought to prevent damage to blood cells, prevent blood clots, and reduce LDL cholesterol (the so-called bad cholesterol).

- Food constituents such as resveratrol are regulators of epigenetic changes. While the research is still in the early stages, promising epigenetic cancer therapies are currently being tested that use resveratrol or curcumin, which is a component of turmeric.

Suggested Reading

Paul, *Origins*.

Questions

1. How did birth records from the Dutch Hunger Winter provide data on generational effects of substandard nutrition during pregnancy?

2. What is a thrifty metabolism, and how is it related to disease patterns?

LECTURE
30

CIVILIZATION: DIETS
AND DISEASES

The relationship between humans and our diseases has changed dramatically over the past 10,000 years. The first epidemiological transition coincided with the development of agriculture around 10,000 years ago and was linked to the domestication of plants and animals. It was characterized by a rise of infectious and nutritional diseases that we still see in various degrees today. The first transition was addressed earlier In this course; this lecture will focus on the second and third epidemiological transitions.

The Second Epidemiological Transition

- The second epidemiological transition has occurred over the last 2 centuries and is characterized by a decline in infectious disease and a rise in chronic degenerative diseases, such as heart disease, diabetes, high blood pressure, asthma, and even some types of cancer. It is timed from the mid-1800s to the present but is really taking off in the mid-20th century.

- The third epidemiological transition is the emergence and reemergence of drug-resistant infectious diseases, such as Ebola and Zika. It is characterized by a resurgence of highly virulent infectious diseases that are affecting populations at a very large scale, along with a suite of novel diseases. It is timed from about the mid-1970s to now.

- Epidemiology is the study of disease patterns, so these transitions highlight a shift in the patterning of disease—but, interestingly, this doesn't mean that when we hit the third transition, the diseases in the second transition disappeared. The overall pattern of diseases that we see in the world today is a combination of health risks that are characterized by both the second and third transitions.

- The second epidemiological transition is how acute infectious diseases gave way to chronic health disorders that are likely related to our current lifestyle—one of minimal physical activity coupled with a diet that's dominated by easy-to-access, highly processed, energy-dense foods.

- Despite lack of modern medical interventions, contraception, or vaccines, the urban working class in the mid-Victorian era were quite healthy, thanks to their good-quality diet. This changed rather quickly by 1870, when high-sugar and high-salt processed foods entered into the diet. With this change in diet came changes in health, life expectancy, and even height.

- Before the Industrial Revolution, which took place from about 1760 until about 1840, people were largely employed in agriculture, either as self-employed farmers or as agricultural laborers. By 1870, machine jobs were taking over the industry, and diets were composed of high-fat and high-sugar foods. This combination marks the beginning of the second epidemiological transition.

- In the United States, weight consciousness emerged as early as 1890. But it wasn't until the turn of the 20th century that poor diet and sedentism, which in this sense means lack of exercise, were moving into public awareness. The start of the pre-packaged food craze in the United States occurred during World War II, when women went into the workforce as men were overseas.

- Prepackaged, processed food did not really hit its heyday, however, until after the war, when the United States moved into the suburban era. Neighborhoods became car centric, built around the idea that everyone would drive to their destinations. And living rooms became TV centric, with meals being consumed more frequently in front of the television.

- The first prepackaged dinners went on the market in 1950 and were oven-ready chicken and turkey potpies that were sold in aluminum trays. They were sold by Swanson, an American food conglomerate that was founded in the late 1800s. In 1953, Swanson invented the TV dinner, which mapped onto suburban living quite well.

- The meals were heated in oven-safe containers until 1986, when microwavable-safe containers hit the market. Today, almost all TV dinners are made for the microwave, and the TV dinner industry is a multibillion-dollar enterprise.

- But it isn't the fact that they are prepackaged that expanded health concerns—and waistlines—starting in the 1960s. It was how they were packaged and preserved.

- Once the trays are filled with foods, the meals are cryogenically frozen, which decreases the chances that it will get spoiled and causes little-to-no damage of the shapes of the individual food pieces. This freezing process, however, is problematic because it

reduces flavor, and companies add more fat, salt, and sugar to the foods to compensate. In addition, some companies use food preservatives to extend the life of the product.

- Coupled with TV dinners, America also saw the invention of fast food. The first fast-food restaurant was A&W, which began as a root beer stand in 1919 in Lodi, California, and shortly thereafter became a drive-in restaurant in Sacramento, California.

- The Pig Stands out of Dallas, Texas, are credited with the first drive-up window—in 1921—and patrons would drive from all around the area to consume their famous barbeque sandwiches. By the late 1940s, drive-throughs were popping up all around the country. The first McDonald's drive-through didn't show up until 1975.

- The rise of fast, processed, and calorically dense food mapped onto declines in physical fitness and activity. America was already concerned with the health risks of being overweight by the early 1960s. Along with fast and convenient foods came a decline in health that mapped onto chronic degenerative diseases—diseases that are still plaguing us today.

- In 2016, the Centers for Disease Control estimated that more than 1/3 of Americans are obese and that obesity-related conditions, such as type 2 diabetes, heart disease, stroke, and some types of cancer, are among the leading causes of preventable death. It also includes the rise of autoimmune diseases, such as asthma.

- During the last half of the 20th century, the world saw a sharp increase in the rate of allergies and diseases of the immune system. One argument for this sharp increase may be explained by the hygiene hypothesis, which proposes that in high-income nations, there is a lack of childhood exposure to symbiotic microorganisms and infectious pathogens.

- This lack of exposure—made all the more severe with sanitized water supplies, sewer systems, and the use of antibiotics—increases susceptibility to allergies by suppressing the development of the immune system.

- The second epidemiological transition, which we are still currently in, has seen a decrease in infectious disease in the postindustrialized West, and increasingly in the developing world, but an increase in autoimmune and allergic diseases.

- In the late 1990s, about 1 in 5 children in industrialized countries were diagnosed with an allergic disease such as asthma or atopic dermatitis. These numbers have skyrocketed, doubling or tripling in the last 3 decades. The incidences of inflammatory bowel diseases, such as ulcerative colitis and Crohn's disease, are also on the rise.

- Interestingly, in the countries where they still suffer from many parasitic diseases, people appear not to be suffering from the same types of autoimmune diseases as people in the postindustrialized West. Once they eradicate those common infections, as we are seeing in some African countries, the rates of such allergic and autoimmune diseases rise.

- The lack of diversity in our gut microbiome might be linked with some of these diseases. New research on celiac disease and gluten sensitivity indicate that there may be a link between the symptoms of gluten-related diseases and the human microbiome.

- As our scientific understanding of the bacterial world increases, so, too, does the support for the hygiene hypothesis. It's important to note, however, that the causal links are not definitive and research continues.

- Many public health messages now urge people to change aspects of their lifestyle to combat many of the diseases associated with the second epidemiological transition. This means eating as healthy as possible, with a diet that includes fresh plants and fermented and high-fiber foods.

- Researchers also suggest regular exercise; limiting the use of antibiotics, hand sanitizers, and antibacterial soaps; and even just opening a window. The simple act of letting the outside in can help bolster your bacterial colonies.

The Third Epidemiological Transition

- The third transition began at the end of the 20th century and continues to the present. It is a global phenomenon that is associated with all of the diseases that were present in the second transition as well as some new ones.

- All around the world, the epidemiological transitions are happening at different rates. Some small-scale societies are only experiencing the second transition, whereas people in the United States are experiencing both the second and the third—and the third includes diseases from the first transition.

- For example, infectious diseases that we thought we had eradicated, such as tuberculosis, are now making a comeback. The National Institutes of Health links this with the existence of antibiotic-resistant pathogens, which might mean that we are at the end of the antibiotic era.

- The World Health Organization declared tuberculosis a world emergency, as it now affects more than 10 million people a year worldwide. We have seen a steady rise in cases over the past 10 years, a trend that epidemiologists predict will continue.

- After decades of no research, because tuberculosis was thought to have been largely eradicated in the postindustrialized West, there is currently a resurgence in scientific research. This is, in part, due to funding from philanthropists Bill and Melinda Gates.

- Many of the diseases are so-called zoonoses, infectious diseases originally from animals that can be transmitted to humans. This is something that characterized the first epidemiological transition and one that is also characterizing the third. One of the most well-known examples is Ebola.

- According to the World Health Organization, Ebola virus disease, formerly known as Ebola haemorrhagic fever, is transmitted from wild animals and spreads through human-to-human contact. Ebola first appeared in 1976 in what is now South Sudan and the Democratic Republic of Congo.

- More recently, there was a massive outbreak in West Africa that began in 2014 and remains the largest and most complex Ebola outbreak in history. The hardest-hit countries include Liberia, Guinea, and Sierra Leone—all countries that have weak health systems and lack human and infrastructural resources.

- Fruit bats are thought to be the natural Ebola virus hosts. The virus is contracted initially from close contact with the blood, organs, or bodily fluids of animals that are infected. These include monkeys, apes, antelope, and porcupines—typically found ill or dead or in the rainforest.

- The virus is then spread through human-to-human contact with blood, organs, or other bodily fluids of an infected person. It can also be spread from contact with surfaces contaminated with these fluids.

- It is important to understand what diseases compose this third epidemiological transition, as many medical researchers argue that the reemergence of infectious disease is a reality. Zika is one example. The disease was first identified in monkeys in Uganda in

1947 and then in humans in 1952. The first outbreak was in 2007 in Micronesia on the Island of Yap.

- It is primarily spread by a particular genus of mosquitoes, *Aedes*, that bites during the day and night. It is also passed from a pregnant woman to her fetus, which is why the World Health Organization was urging pregnant women to avoid mosquitoes at all costs during the most recent outbreak.

- Children born with the virus have a birth defect called microcephaly, where their heads are considerably smaller than their counterparts without the virus. They often have brains that are not fully developed; in severe cases, children with microcephaly also have issues with vision, speech, hearing, locomotion, and balance.

- There is currently no vaccine—just as with Ebola—and research continues at a rapid pace to, hopefully, find prevention in the future.

Suggested Reading

Pollan, *The Omnivore's Dilemma*.
Schlosser, *Fast Food Nation*.

Questions

1. What are the diseases that are associated with the third epidemiological transition, and which transition are we in now?

2. How do the history of prepackaged foods, suburban living, and fast-food restaurants map onto the rise of obesity in American history?

LECTURE
31

WHAT THE WORLD
IS EATING

The act of sitting down for a meal with family and friends is a global tradition, but what this meal looks like around the world is strikingly different. In this lecture, you will discover what the world is currently eating. While it's impossible to provide comprehensive information on what every population or geographic region eats, shifting cultural trends and how they map onto our food choices can be addressed.

Global Nutrition

- In an ambitious project called *Hungry Planet*, writer Faith D'Aluisio and photographer Peter Menzel traveled the world in the early 2000s to document what the world was eating. In a stunning series of photographs, they captured images of 24 families from around the world and the typical diet that family would consume in an average week.

- The book was published in 2005, and in 2013, the images were exhibited by the Nobel Peace Center in Oslo, Norway, in an attempt to raise global awareness about the cost, content, calories, and cultural significance of different cuisines around the world.

- A week's worth of food for the Aboubakars, a family of 6 living in a Sudanese refugee camp in Chad, included sorghum, maize, goat meat, fish, limes, legumes, red onions, garlic, okra, red chili peppers, tomatoes, and a ration of sunflower oil, sugar, salt, ginger, and about 77 gallons of water provided by the aid organization Oxfam International. The market value of all of their food if purchased in the United States would be approximately $1.22.

- A week's worth of food for the Ahmeds, a family of 11 living in Cairo, Egypt, included a wide variety of grains and other starches, dairy products, animal products, fruits and vegetables, and condiments. They drank soda, tea, and water that was used for both consumption and cooking. The market value of all of their food if purchased in the United States would be approximately $68.53.

- A week's worth of food for the Madsens, a family of 5 living in Cape Hope village in Greenland, included typical Danish food, such as meatballs, sausage, ham, liver paste, soup, muesli, pasta, bread, potato crisps, fruit candy, chocolate bars, and soda, coffee, and tea. Their weekly meals also included more typical Inuit foods, such as musk ox, walrus, polar pear, and narwhal oil. The market value of all of their food if purchased in the United States would be approximately $277.04.

- A week's worth of food for the Aymes, a family of 9 living in Ecuador, included grains and starches, fruits and vegetables, and almost no animal products—only a few gallons of milk from the family cows. Other beverages included water from a spring near to their home and wild stinging nettle tea. The market value of all of their food if purchased in the United States would be approximately $31.55.

- The photos do an excellent job of providing visual imagery on the array of different types of foods that people all around the world eat. In addition to showing this variation, we can also see differences in quantity and cost of the foods that are routinely consumed.

- In terms of total caloric intake, the book does not provide comparative information that can be easily tracked family by family. Even if they did, it is important to note that these are snapshots of individual families around the world and are not meant to be indicative of what every member of that community, culture, or country eats. Rather, the photographs offer a window into viewing the wide range of foods that people eat.

- The team also published another book more recently called *What I Eat: Around the World in 80 Diets*, in which they photodocumented the daily diet of 80 different people from 80 different walks of life.

- But for us to say anything about global nutrition, we need data on calorie content. And for that, we can turn to recent data generated by National Geographic on their website. They launched an interactive tool that allows visitors to their site to click on a country in the world and see how portions have changed over the last 50 years and the calorie amount that different types of food contribute to the daily diet.

- In the United States, for example, with data based on 2011, they calculated that the average daily diet consisted of about 3641 calories. The U.S. Department of Agriculture recommends that moderately active adults between the ages of 41 and 60 years old consume about 2600 calories a day for men and 2000 calories a day for women.

- They divided these calories in the following way: 36% sugar and fat, 22% grain, 14% dairy and eggs, 13% meat, 8% produce, and about 6% other.

- Other countries that were estimated to be similar, both in terms of daily caloric intake and composition of diet, are the United Kingdom, Australia, Germany, Spain, Brazil, Russia, Argentina, and Cuba.

- Interestingly, South Korea was similar in terms of overall calories and most of the food categories, but they swapped out dairy and eggs and consumed more grains. North Korea, on the other hand, was estimated to be about 63% grains, with only 5% coming from meat and 1% coming from eggs and dairy. Their average daily caloric intake, at 2103 calories, was more than 1000 calories less than South Korea, who consume an average of 3329 calories a day.

Calories

- The standard unit of measurement in nutrition is called a kilocalorie, or kcal. Many non-nutritionists and the public often use the abbreviated term "calorie" for short. The problem is that 1 kcal is actually equivalent to 1 Calorie, what nutritionists call a big calorie or 1000 small calories.

- By the early 20th century, the word "calorie," irrespective of capitalization and actually referring to kilocalorie, was already in widespread use—both in nutritional policy and in the public. This has led to many misuses and misunderstandings of food-energy units and their abbreviations.

- When we talk about "calories," we are really talking about kilocalories, even though the parlance is to say calorie. This is only really an issue if you are reading nutrition literature. For most of people, who are mostly reading food labels, it is less confusing.

- Using calories as our currency, the world's top consumers include the United States topping the list, followed closely by Austria, Italy, Israel, Ireland, and the United Kingdom.

Japanese Cuisine

- While it would be impossible to take a comprehensive world tour of individual cuisines, we can choose a few cuisines to explore. The few that we'll examine are listed by the United Nations as part of the world's "intangible cultural heritage."

- According to the UNESCO website, this heritage can include objects but also extends to performing arts, rituals, festivals, oral traditions, social practices, and knowledge and skills concerning nature, the universe, or the production of traditional crafts. Many things included as intangible cultural heritage are associated with cuisine and culinary traditions around the world.

- One fascinating example comes from Japan and is called *washoku*, which the UNESCO website defines as "a social practice based on a set of skills, knowledge, practice and traditions related to the production, processing, preparation and consumption of food."

- It focuses on the consumption of natural, locally sourced ingredients, such as rice, fish, and vegetables. It includes pickled vegetables; soups made with tofu, kelp, and miso; and sides of cooked tofu, vegetables, or fish.

- Many enthusiasts of this type of food preparation claim that the traditional basic structure includes 1 soup, 1 main dish, and 2 additional side dishes. Today, there are many different variations on the theme that are based on seasonal and regional differences.

- This type of food preparation is incorporated into other types of quintessentially Japanese cuisine: bento boxes (boxes that contain single-portion meals) and sushi. Today, bento boxes are incredibly popular the world over, and sushi has become somewhat of an American institution.

Mexican Cuisine

- Another cuisine that is listed by UNESCO as intangible world heritage is traditional Mexican cuisine. The United Nations group states on their website that it is not just food but the behaviors that accompany them.

- From farming and culinary and ritual practices to ancestral customs, all of it is included in traditional cuisine that involves the whole food chain—from production to preparation to presentation. One of the main staples of Mexican food is the tortilla, which has been a mainstay of the diet in North American and Mesoamerican cuisine for almost 1000 years.

- Maize, which was the basis for the original tortillas, is a crop that is one of the so-called 3 sisters: the inclusive group of maize, beans, and squash that were part of the classic Native American mixed-crops system.

- Archaeological evidence suggests that these 3 domesticates have been routinely grown together for around 5000 years. The 3 crops were originally planted close together because they benefitted one another.

- The 3 sisters are a terrific combination of nutrition. They provide requisite amino acids to make complete proteins when you eat all 3 together. The bean species that were first grown in Mexico included common beans as well as teppary beans, which are native to the southwestern United States and Mexico.

- Mexican cuisine varies by region and has, like Japanese food, become a mainstay of the American diet.

French Cuisine

- Other diets that made the UNESCO list of intangible cultural heritage of humanity include the Mediterranean diet, the tradition of kimchi making in Korea, bread baking in Armenia, beer making in Belgium, and the gastronomic meal of the French.

- From the UNESCO website, the French gastronomic meal "emphasizes togetherness, the pleasure of taste, and the balance between human beings and the products of nature." Key elements include purchasing and preparing local and seasonal foods that are then paired with wine.

- French meals often begin with an aperitif, a drink before the meal, and end with an after-dinner liqueur. The meal itself is composed of several courses, typically at least 3 or 4, that include a starter, fish or meat with vegetables, cheese, and dessert.

- Today, an estimated 2 cookbooks per day are published in France. And with more than 5000 French restaurants in the city of Paris alone, there are many people in France and abroad that want to prepare and eat traditional French dishes.

- One of the most well-known French dishes is escargot, or snails. While this small gastropod might be seen as a backyard pest in the United States, in most other parts of the world, they are a delicacy. Prepared in their shells with ingredients such as cream, butter, garlic, and parsley, they are delicious as well as popular.

- Another food item that is often associated with French cuisine is cheese. Food experts claim that there are anywhere from 300 to 1000 different varietals of French cheese. Every region of the country has certain cheeses that it is associated with, and looking for a comprehensive list can be exhausting.

- There are 4 classifications of French cheese that all of the types fall into: farmhouse cheeses, which are produced on the farm where the milk used to make the cheese is also produced; artisanal cheeses, where the manufacturer of the cheese does so in very small amounts using milk from either their own farm or other local farms; cooperative cheeses, which are made with milk from local dairies that have joined together to produce fairly large quantities; and industrial cheeses, which are factory produced from milk that is either sourced locally or regionally.

Suggested Reading

Menzel and D'Aluisio, *Hungry Planet*.
———, *What I Eat*.
Pollan, *The Omnivore's Dilemma*.

Questions

1. How does the average daily caloric intake in the United States map onto the U.S. Department of Agriculture recommendations?

2. What is an example of cuisine listed by the United Nations as intangible world heritage?

LECTURE
32

THE OVERNUTRITION
EPIDEMIC

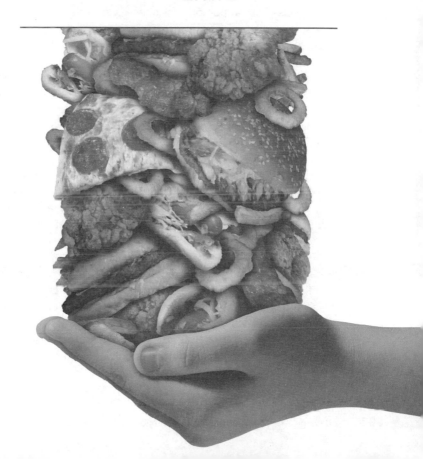

Overnutrition is a global epidemic. According to the World Health Organization (WHO), most of the world's population now lives in countries where obesity kills more people than malnutrition. This lecture will focus on the health consequences of being obese and will explore the 2-pronged pathway to global obesity today: decreased physical activity and changes in diet.

Body Mass Index

- What classifies a person as obese can often be difficult to measure, so the WHO has posted global indicators that quantify excessive fat accumulation based on body mass index (BMI).

- While it is not a direct measurement of body fat, many medical professionals argue that BMI does tend to correlate with body fat and is typically used as an indicator that a person is overweight. The formula for the calculation is weight in kilograms divided by height in meters squared.

- The WHO's cutoff for being overweight is having a BMI that is greater than or equal to 25, and the cutoff for obesity is having a BMI that is greater than or equal to 30. The American Heart Association lists a BMI between 18.5 and 25 as an indication of normal weight and a BMI under 18 as an indicator of being underweight.

- But these estimates should be taken with some caution. Some nutritionists and metabolic researchers argue that BMI is far from ideal and that other measurements, such as skinfold thickness or underwater weighing, may be more accurate. In addition, researchers argue that BMI is less than ideal because it cannot distinguish between fat and muscle or between different types of fat.

- Duel-energy x-ray absorptiometry is more accurate—as it is able to distinguish between fat, bone, and muscle mass—but it is also very costly, which is part of the reason why BMI remains the most common tool used to screen for underweight, healthy weight, overweight, or obese.

- If a person's BMI is out of the healthy range, whether under or over, his or her health risks are likely to increase. These include cardiovascular disease, diabetes, osteoarthritis, and some types of cancer.

Physical Inactivity

- The primary cause of obesity and being overweight is thought to be an energy imbalance between the number of calories consumed and the number of calories expended. Global rates of obesity have been linked to decreases in physical activity coupled with increases in the consumption of fatty energy-dense foods.

- Declines in physical activity have been linked to several shifts in behavioral patterns and technology over the last 100 years. One of the major shifts was when cars became the predominant form of transportation.

- The ubiquity of cars combined with the rise of suburban neighborhoods meant more time spent in cars and less time walking. Couple this with changes in technology in the workplace and more time sitting down at a desk—or, since the 1980s, in front of a computer screen—and you get a rapid increase in sedentism, which is a pattern of physical inactivity.

- It is estimated that today, the average American spends 8.5 hours a day in front of some type of screen. It can feel almost impossible to escape screens; they're everywhere. People can do almost anything online, including shopping, attending virtual meetings, and taking courses—and all of it from the comfort of their own couch.

- Participation in community sports has also declined over the past several decades. Adult recreational league sports are rapidly declining, and something that used to be common, the company softball team, is now almost nonexistent. And it's not just softball. It includes 5K runs, dodgeball, basketball, and any other team recreational sport.

- This also extends to youth sports. The National Alliance for Youth Sports in the United States conducted a wide-ranging poll and found that most American children quit team sports by the time they are around 13 years old.

- Screen time for children is increasing. We also live in a world where play—simple, unrestricted play—is no longer encouraged. We tether our children to desks, tablets, tables, and tests all day. Compounding the issue is that fewer and fewer kids walk or ride their bikes to school; more often they are riding to school in cars or buses.

- All of these factors work in concert with one another to reduce physical activity. In addition, sedentism and screen time may have additional negative consequences for behavior, attention span, and physical health.

- In the past 30 years, rates of obesity in children have doubled and quadrupled in adolescence, according to the Centers for Disease Control. A recent estimate on their website suggests that more than 1/3 of children and teenagers in the United States are currently overweight or obese.

- In addition to the same risk factors seen in overweight and obese adults, including cardiovascular disease, high blood pressure, and some types of cancer, children and teenagers also exhibit higher risk for type 2 diabetes and prediabetes. They're also at higher risk for sleep apnea, bone and joint problems, and psychological problems, such as low self-esteem.

- Lack of physical activity is a big factor in why our children are becoming more and more overweight, and our lack of physical activity is at a mismatch with the conditions in which we evolved. Research suggests that cardiovascular health is connected with physical activity and was likely a key part of the evolution of our physiology.

Diet Composition

- We are now eating 3 times the amount of sugar that we ate 30 years ago. According to several estimates, the average American eats more than 60 pounds of sugar a year, not including fruits and fruit juices.

- Glucose is something that we need. During our evolutionary history, it is likely that a shot of sugar, such as honey, had positive effects on the expansion of our brains. This is because our brains use glucose as fuel that powers billions of neuronal nerve cells.

- Our brains handle different types of sugar differently. Glucose can help suppress the part of our brain that makes us want to eat, while fructose does the opposite. According to neurological experiments done after eating both types, fructose amplifies the reward centers of our brain, making us want it more.

- We get the bulk of our fructose in foods sweetened with high-fructose corn syrup and from sweetened drinks, syrups, and dessert foods. High-fructose corn syrup is absorbed quickly, so it does not stimulate the production of leptin or insulin. This is the mechanism at play that triggers the body's signals for satiation, which is what can lead to overeating.

- The Department of Agriculture estimates that the average American consumes about 27 pounds of high-fructose corn syrup a year. Some estimates suggest that 1 in 5 Americans drink at least one soda every day; other estimates suggest that half of Americans currently drink soda on a daily basis.

- Despite these high numbers, Americans are actually reducing their soda consumption. There has been a national move toward reducing the intake of soda. The U.S. soda habit is currently at the lowest level in 30 years, and the trend is continuing downward. Many companies have reduced their 64-ounce soda cups—not as a reaction against the sugar or calorie content, but because they don't fit in car cup holders.

- The other sugary drinks that people turn to in lieu of soda are energy drinks and iced teas. Most iced teas, while seemingly a healthy alternative, can contain 60 grams of sugar and 250 calories. Energy drinks are also not a healthy option; many of the most popular brands have as many calories and grams of sugar as soda or more.

- Coffee drinks can also contain a surprising number of calories and sugar. Some coffee drinks can even contain more calories than a fast-food burger.

- Beyond calorie-rich foods and sweet beverages, another contributing factor is portion size. The "super size" phenomenon has been written about extensively in nutrition research as well as in the popular media. Portion sizes have changed drastically over the last several decades. The average American eats about 25% more today than they did in the early 1970s. Plates themselves have also increased in size.

- Nutritionists are urging people to attempt to shift their portions and plates back to the size they were in the 1950s. Other recommendations to combat large portions include using a larger plate for salad as long as your main course is on a small plate. Other tips include not placing food at the table during meals, as it encourages second helpings; refraining from watching TV while you eat; and limiting eating out to about once a week.

- When you do eat out at a restaurant, nutrition experts urge people to order vegetables and protein, avoiding carbohydrates as much as possible, and suggest getting a to-go box at the beginning of a meal and taking half of the meal home.

- Mayo Clinic provides some handy tricks for people who are unsure of what proper serving sizes might be—not the serving sizes listed on the back of food packaging, as those are based on the amount of food people tend to actually eat, not the amount of food they are recommended to eat.

- To help combat this confusing food-labeling and portion-sizing conundrum, Mayo Clinic suggests memorizing the average size of some everyday items to aid in estimating portion size. For example, one vegetable serving is about the size of a baseball while a serving of meat should be about the same size as a deck of cards.

- Most people are not aware that we are experiencing this phenomenon of portion distortion, as they focus on the serving sizes listed on packaging. It seems like the true enemy in the global war on obesity changes often—from fat to sugar to additives, for example—making it difficult to know precisely what might be to blame for the pandemic we are experiencing now. It is likely a combination of changes in diet, shifting toward processed, fatty, energy-dense foods in a world where physical activity levels are declining rapidly.

Suggested Reading

Pollan, *The Omnivore's Dilemma*.
Schlosser, *Fast Food Nation*.

Questions

1. How was the rise of the suburban lifestyle associated with sedentism (lack of physical activity) and obesity in U.S. history?

2. How is obesity related to cardiovascular and metabolic diseases?

LECTURE
33

WORLD POVERTY
AND UNDERNUTRITION

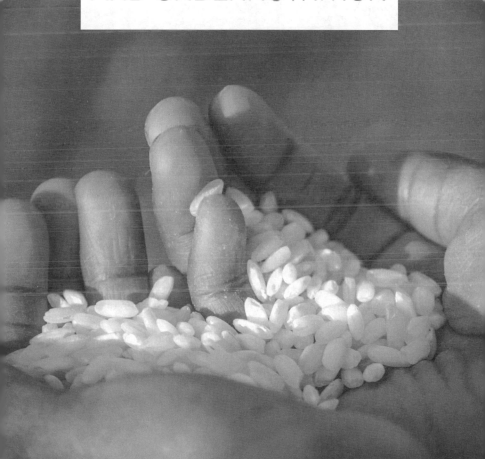

W hile many in the world have enough—or even too much—to eat, there are still hundreds of millions of people who go to bed hungry every night. Undernutrition accounts for a fairly large percentage of the global burden of disease and is considered by many medical health professionals to be the number-one risk to health worldwide. In addition, health complications associated with undernutrition kill more people each year than malaria, AIDS, and tuberculosis combined.

Malnutrition

- For several decades, reducing poverty around the world has been a top welfare objective. More recently, the focus has shifted to distinguishing between food insecurity, monetary poverty, and nutrition status. These are critical distinctions because while these things are typically related, they each reveal a particular vulnerability.

- They are often best dealt with using specific tools meant to target the population or country in question. The realization that different countries and economies may require different plans of action has altered the landscape of programs aimed to end global poverty.

- For example, researchers now realize that there are several malnutrition indicators that go far beyond simple diet composition. Agricultural productivity, fertility rates, literacy rates, disease profiles, and gross domestic product per capita are all factors that tend to indicate the nutritional status of a given country or population—whether that nutritional status is good or bad.

- A combination of low rates of literacy and high rates of fertility, for example, tends to map on to both monetary poverty and malnutrition. High gross domestic product per capita tends to translate into diseases of civilization and obesity-related disorders. The disease burden faced by a given population is often linked to its nutrition profile, whether it be overnutrition or undernutrition.

- Even when adequate food supply exists, not all calories are created equal. New research on global aims to reduce poverty have found that lack of dietary diversity is another indicator that tends to map onto malnutrition. In addition, another factor to contend with is the idea of a diet based on empty calories, even when you are getting a lot of them. Malnutrition can be either undernutrition or overnutrition.

- It's important to distinguish between hunger and malnutrition. Hunger is the way that our body signals to us that we need to eat. It subsides once we have eaten enough food to satisfy our hunger. Hunger can be associated with malnutrition, but lack of hunger does not necessarily mean lack of malnutrition.

- There are typically 2 types of malnourishment that are associated with undernutrition: protein-energy malnutrition and dietary deficiencies. There are 2 different types of protein-energy malnutrition: kwashiorkor, lack of enough protein; and marasmus, lack of enough protein and calories.

- Symptoms of kwashiorkor include a characteristic distended belly from an enlarged liver, loss of muscle mass, failure to grow or gain weight, changes in skin pigment, and chronic lethargy. It most often occurs in areas where there is limited food supply or famine. While this condition is rare in the United States, it does occur— most notably among the elderly living in nursing homes, where they eat diets that are often lacking in enough protein.

- Symptoms of marasmus include severe loss of muscle mass and subcutaneous fat, unusual changes in body temperature, dehydration, anemia, pneumonia, and, in extreme cases, corneal lesions or heart failure. It's caused by severe deficiencies in macronutrients, including protein, carbohydrates, and fats. This type of starvation is commonly seen among the world's poorest citizens living in the developing world.

- In addition to these 2 types of protein-energy malnutrition, there are also dietary deficiencies. Micronutrient deficiencies include the lack of enough essential vitamins and minerals, such as iron, iodine, zinc, vitamin A, and vitamin D. Micronutrient deficiencies can have devastating health consequences.

- In addition to micronutrient deficiencies, undernutrition also includes stunting, which occurs during critical periods of growth and development during infancy and childhood. Stunting is associated with an underdeveloped brain, reduced mental ability and learning capacity, and increased risks of chronic diseases, such as diabetes, hypertension, and obesity, in adulthood.

- Micronutrient deficiencies are sometimes called hidden hunger because people might get enough calories—sometimes too many calories—and not necessarily know that they are lacking certain essential micronutrients.

- The disease-scape is changing with the emergence of new disease burdens in which people in poverty-stricken areas are actually overweight or even obese. They're consuming lots of calories and are consequently overweight, but they are nevertheless malnourished. This concept, dubbed "plump poverty" by Dr. Claudia Chaufan, is associated with the fourth nutrition transition.

- Plump poverty is something that happens right at the boundary of the third and fourth nutrition transition stages, when people are coming out of calorie-poor diets coupled with malnutrition and moving into calorie-rich diets coupled with undernutrition due to nutrient deficiencies in the diet.

- But there is also an added factor of developmental programming that is associated with global malnourishment. When a mother is calorie restricted or nutrient deficient during pregnancy, her developing infant will respond to her poor-quality diet by preparing for a life in childhood and adulthood that mirrors the uterine environment.

- Their so-called thrifty metabolism then encounters a nutritional environment in the outside world that is not nutritionally restricted, and their metabolism turns those extra calories into visceral fat and excessive sugar in the bloodstream.

- In the case of plump poverty, there are enough calories but too few nutrients. Mothers who are very poor and can only afford low-quality foods are gearing the metabolisms of their children for cardiometabolic diseases later in life.

- So, there are multiple pathways for this developmental programming: One is a calorie-restricted diet that might be nutrient adequate, and the other is a nutrient-restricted diet that is calorie abundant.

- You can also have the scenario in which a mother has the worst of both worlds: where she is eating a diet that is both calorically restricted and nutrient poor. All of these can lead to plump poverty via developmental programming

Poor Living Conditions

- When most people think about urbanization, we think of progress—but they are not synonymous. In fact, the United Nations (UN) estimates that about half of the world's populations are currently living in cities and towns, and 1 out of 3 of these urban dwellers is living in slum conditions.

- Some estimates suggest that about 15 million people are also living in city dumps. This number is shocking, but it pales in comparison to the number of people living in the world's slums, which is thought to be about 1 billion.

- The UN defines a slum as a household that lacks one of the following conditions: access to improved water, access to improved sanitation, sufficient living space, durability of housing, or security of tenure.

- People who reside in slums often suffer from unemployment, illiteracy, drug addiction, and, in extreme cases, high rates of mortality. In addition, the overcrowded and unhygienic conditions create a veritable breeding ground for communicable and waterborne diseases, which can often lead to the rise of an epidemic, given the right parameters.

- Compounding the issue of disease transmission is the fact that many people living in slums have migrated from rural areas, where they developed little or no immunity to urban diseases they face once they reach the cities.

- Today, urban slums are considered to be the fastest-growing human habitat. The world is also facing an unprecedented situation where refugee camps are essentially functioning as urban slums.

- According the UN Refugee Agency, 2016 saw an all-time high of displaced people. The total number of displaced people in the world was 65.3 million, with 21.3 million of these people being classified as refugees—those who were forced to leave their homes due to conflict and persecution.

- Estimates suggest that a little more half of these refugees are placed into camps, temporary settlements that are built to meet basic human needs for only short periods of time.

- Doctors Without Borders has labeled the malnutrition in refugee camps as "catastrophic." One of the reasons that starvation is so rampant is because people residing in the camps are almost entirely reliant on humanitarian aid. In addition to simply not having enough to eat, much of the food provided does not offer adequate nutrition.

Reducing Poverty and Hunger

- In an effort to diversify the diet to include fresh food and to attempt to curb malnutrition, the UN has teamed up with the World Food Programme to create multistory gardens in refugee camps. In the camps where they have been introduced, such as in Dadaab and Kakuma located in Kenya, they have been a great success. However, they only work as long as the support for them continues. The 2 camps where this ingenious system was tried out may be disbanded.

- The UN has convened a program called UN-Habitat that is specifically targeted at improving the quality of life of people living in urban slums.

- There has been a phenomenal shift toward urbanization in the past few decades, with 6 out of every 10 people in the world expected to reside in urban areas by the year 2030. Given this situation, the UN General Assembly has mandated addressing urban growth.

- The General Assembly advocates a holistic approach that works to upgrade slums with improved access to basic municipal services and increased access to services and opportunities. Most community projects are initiated at the neighborhood level, as participation of the communities in question tends to increase their viability. UN-Habitat is actively working toward more cost-effective and energy-efficient technologies.

- While poverty rates are declining, it is happening at a different pace in different regions around the world. Within the last decade, the poverty rate in East Asia and the Pacific was reduced by 71 million people, most notably in China and Indonesia. In South Asia, the rate was reduced by 37 million, most notably in India. However, half of the world's poverty stricken live in sub-Saharan Africa, with a drop of only about 4 million within the last decade.

- There is a worldwide effort to reduce and eliminate hunger, not just in the postindustrialized West. One of the U.S.-based institutions that works to sustainably end hunger and reduce poverty is based in Washington DC and is called the International Food Policy Research Institute. It was established in 1975 with the explicit goal to help reduce world poverty and undernutrition.

- Like many aid organizations, the institute argues that some of the answers to this global dilemma are to consistently support local farmers, boost infant health and nutrition in developing countries, and—a much more controversial solution—possibly introduce genetically modified foods and stem-cell meat.

- During the next handful of decades, world food production must increase to meet growing demands. This will require not only increased production of resources, but also more efficient water, land, and energy use.

- There are other solutions that are also proving to be quite effective. While the ultimate goal would be for the entire world to be self-sustaining, this is a slow process and not realizable in the short term. Meanwhile, donations are critical. While many people want to donate food directly, this can be logistically difficult.

- Donating food at your local food bank can be incredibly helpful. But don't give anything that you would not want to eat, and don't give anything that is perishable. Try to include things that don't require heating or opening with a can opener. Aid organizations also suggest calling your local food bank to inquire what they need.

- Several organizations are based on donations. During the fiscal year of 2016, the Feeding America Network provided 4 billion meals in the United States. On a global scale, Feed the Children, a nonprofit relief organization based in the United States, is very successful. In addition to providing nutrition, donations also go to deworming children around the world. They focus on both long-term medical care and on empowering mothers.

Suggested Reading

Davis, "Planet of Slums."

Questions

1. How does undernutrition contribute to the global burden of disease?

2. What are the 2 types of malnourishment that are associated with undernutrition?

LECTURE
34

SHOULD THE WORLD
EAT MEAT?

The meat-production industry provides a livelihood for billions of people, but it also comes with a hefty price tag in terms of health consequences for the consumer and environmental consequences for the planet. This lecture is about the politics of meat and asks the question of whether sustainable meat production is a myth or a reality. You will learn about the environmental costs of producing meat, the different types of meat production currently in use around the world, and the likelihood that meat consumption will decline or that we'll find new ways to produce enough to meet the growing demand.

Meat Production

- While the world's appetite is growing, the planet is not. According to the Food and Agriculture Organization (FAO) of the United Nations, about 60% of the world's ice-free land surface is currently dedicated to raising crops and providing grazing land for the animals that we eat, supporting around 360 million cattle and 600 million sheep and goats.

- The FAO estimates that every year, about 13 billion hectares of forest area are lost due to land conversion for the production of both plant food for human consumption as well as livestock feed.

- According to the U.S. Department of Agriculture Economic Research Service, the United States has about 2.3 billion acres of land. Of this total, only about 66 million acres, or 3%, are developed, meaning urban and peri-urban areas.

- Rural residential land, with farmhouses and subdivisions, make up about 73 million acres, and about 747 million acres are forest lands, but about 140 million acres of this land is used for livestock grazing.

- These numbers seem staggering, until you learn the amount of land in the United States that is dedicated to cropland: 349 million acres. Of this land, about 3 million acres are used to grow crops for human consumption. The remainder are used to grow feeder crops for livestock.

- The most recent census of agriculture by the USDA estimates that this totals up to more than 40% of all of the tillable land in the United States, which means the land that is able to be cultivated. The most planted crops in the United States are called feeder crops. These include wheat, soybeans, corn, and alfalfa. And all of these but wheat are primarily grown to feed livestock.

- Many food scientists argue that this level of crop production is unsustainable. There are alternative foods that have been suggested, however, that in the coming decades might gain momentum. These include algae, sugarcane, and so-called brewer's grains, which is the solid residue that's the product of the germinated and dried cereal grains that are used to make beer.

- In addition to coming up with more sustainable feed for livestock, people are trying to come up with ways to make the entire food system, as it pertains to meat, more sustainable. And we have been making strides.

- Compared with the late 1970s, beef production in the United States now requires much fewer resources for the equivalent type of system. Some estimates suggest that to produce 1 billion kilograms of beef, today we are only using about 88% of the water that we did back then, and only about 67% of the land.

- This also extends to waste outputs. The amount of manure, for example, has been reduced by 18% compared to 1977. In addition, the overall carbon footprint per billion kilograms of beef produced in 2007 was reduced by more than 16% compared to the same footprint from the late 1970s.

- But while the numbers might be down, livestock still contributes to greenhouse gas emissions. As of 2017, the FAO had estimated that globally, livestock contributes about 14.5% of all anthropogenic, or human-made, greenhouse gas emissions.

- The majority of these gases are from cows, due to enteric fermentation and manure. Enteric fermentation is a natural part of the digestive process for ruminants, or animals that have a 4-chambered stomach that is designed to ferment plant foods.

- Enteric fermentation is the process by which these types of animals digest carbohydrates. This process produces greenhouse gases. The gases are a by-product of the way that they ferment their food to digest the roughage that they consume.

- The fermentation process causes cows, who are the biggest offender, to belch and pass gas—a lot of gas and all the time. When they do, it produces methane and carbon dioxide. Burps contribute much more than gas.

- Cows have worse belches when they eat certain types of food. When eating a diet based on corn and soy, which is what the majority of livestock diets are, the belching problem is only exacerbated. This is why new research is moving toward changing the diet of these gaseous beasts. Some in the agricultural industry are switching to diets of alfalfa, and some are starting to use supplements that can reduce methane emissions.

- Other ways that the agricultural industry is making strides to reduce the gas output is by improving breeding and the way that animal health interventions are done. The FAO argues that if herd sizes were to shrink, based on such practices, this would mean fewer, yet more productive, livestock.

- In addition to belching and passing gas, cows also produce a lot of manure. It's the end point of their digestion, and it also produces

nitrous oxide. There are many fascinating new practices that are turning manure into electricity—electricity that can then be sold back to the power grid.

- Better management of grazing lands could also greatly improve productivity and potentially aid in offsetting livestock emissions by creating carbon sinks. By simply reducing the amount of space that livestock use for grazing, it can open up natural areas— carbon sinks—that act to suck up and store carbon dioxide from the environment.

- This point about better management of grazing areas is particularly germane to meat politics. The United Nations has argued that people who are most intimately involved in the use of the land must have a voice in how it's used. This is a particularly complicated issue in the developing world.

- Many governments, some of them with the best intentions, have provided fuel and fertilizer subsidies to areas in the Middle East and Africa. These subsidies can carry negative consequences, as they encourage people to convert their pasture land into marginal cropping land.

- There are also several widespread attempts to settle traditional pastoralists, who tend their livestock on noncommercial land all over the developing world. The aim, particularly in places such as Central Asia and the Middle East, is to privatize all farms, which means that small-scale pastoralists will no longer be able to engage in their traditional subsistence practices.

Poultry Production

- Poultry production also poses its own suite of environmental issues. Many experts argue that this is largely tied to the growth of the sector.

- Over the past several decades, there has been a trend toward more intensification and concentration, which has given rise to a number of environmental concerns. The increased intensification is because more of the world is eating more poultry, which includes chicken, turkey, geese, and ducks.

- The reasons for this is because the meat is accessible, convenient, relatively affordable, and easy for the consumer to find and prepare. It also doesn't face as many religious restrictions as pork or beef and is considered by nutritionists to be fairly healthy, low-fat meat.

- Poultry production faces similar challenges to those that affect the livestock industry, such as meeting the demand of the market while dealing with environmental costs.

- Some of the environmental concerns surrounding the poultry industry include landscape degradation due to soil and water pollution, which can come from poor practices in the disposal of poultry carcasses or from water discharge during the slaughtering process.

- The FAO reports that process wastewater used in many facilities may contain high levels of nitrogen, phosphorus, and chlorine, which are chemicals that are used for washing and disinfection.

- The wastewater can also contain drug residues from antimicrobial agents used to treat disease in the birds and pathogens, such as salmonella and campylobacter, which are both foodborne illnesses that can come from raw or undercooked poultry.

- In addition, pathogens and heavy metals are often found in the soil, typically due to poor manure management. Many production sites, however, utilize the manure, which can either be used as fertilizer for cropland or processed into pellets for animal feed, particularly fish and cattle.

- Additional strides are being made. The FAO argues that continued selection for genetically improved and climate-tolerant plant cultivars will only continue. This means that the feed options will expand for more countries, both in the postindustrialized world and elsewhere.

- Better feed, in terms of macronutrient and micronutrient provision, will reduce the nutrient waste that is one of the biggest threats to the environment. Changes in husbandry practices are also being instituted, which support more effective immune responses, which means antibiotic-free poultry.

Fish Production

- Strides in fisheries are also being made. Wild fisheries are often called capture fisheries, whereas farmed fisheries are also known as aquaculture, where the breeding, rearing, and harvesting of fish and shellfish occurs.

- Fish is an important source of protein all around the world, and the FAO argues that fisheries and aquaculture play a large role in eliminating world hunger and reducing poverty. World fish consumption is at an all-time high.

- Beyond that, it's also the main livelihood for millions of people. Over the last 50 years, however, fishing practices are pushing many fish stocks dangerously close to the point of collapse. Many of the problems arise from illegal, unreported, and unregulated fishing and from poor governance.

- The FAO argues, however, that these can be overcome and that the global community is making strides with strategic partnerships and better engagement with both the public and private sectors.

Meat-Based Diets

- The costs of meat production are high. Beyond the environmental costs, a segment of the nutrition science community as well as animal rights activists argue for eliminating meat consumption altogether. Given the global rise in consumption patterns, this doesn't seem to be the most likely future outcome. Given that, it's important to discuss the health consequences of a diet based largely on meat.

- The distinction between red and white meat is determined primarily by the myoglobin content of the meat. Myoglobin is the heme iron that contains pigmented proteins that make meat red in color. The more myoglobin, the redder the meat.

- Beef has much more myoglobin when compared to chicken, which is considered to be a white meat. Red meat has certain characteristics that white meat doesn't, and these can often be associated with negative health outcomes.

- The most common red meats eaten around the world are beef, pork, veal, lamb, mutton, and goat. All of these are great sources of protein, niacin, vitamin B_6, vitamin B_{12}, phosphorous, zinc, and iron. Red meat also contains adequate shares of the essential amino acids and fatty acids. Another benefit is that it's about 94% digestible, so it is highly bioavailable to our bodies.

- Despite these benefits, large-scale red meat consumption is increasingly implicated as contributing toward the global epidemic of cardiovascular diseases, cancer, obesity, and type 2 diabetes. The mechanisms are still being studied, and while the work remains controversial, there is mounting evidence to suggest that eating too much red meat carries significant risk.

- Processed red meat is typically associated with the greatest disease risk. This includes any products that are preserved by methods other than freezing, such as salting, smoking, or marinating. This includes foods such as ham, bacon, sausages, salami, corned beef, or tinned meat.

- Experimental evidence using animal models indicates that some of the nitrates used in meat preservation and their by-products can potentially decrease insulin production, impair glucose tolerance, and lead to atherosclerosis (which is the hardening and narrowing of the arteries and can lead to heart attacks, strokes, or vascular disease).

- Before we stop eating meat altogether, it's important to note that most of the world is actually protein deficient. And red meat is a fantastic source of not only protein but other critical things, such as iron.

- Perhaps the solution, according to many nutritionists, is to eat less meat. This is one of the reasons why people, particularly in the postindustrialized West, are making the choice to turn away from meat. Another reason is political. The vegan movement, for example, is focused on a lifestyle that is not based on using the products of animals.

Suggested Reading

Pollan, *In Defense of Food*.
Pond, Nichols, and Brown, eds., *Adequate Food for All*.

Questions

1. Why is the Food and Agriculture Organization of the United Nations concerned about the growing global consumption of meat?

2. What are some of the ways in which the meat industry is changing its practices to become more sustainable?

SHOULD WE BE
POWERED BY PLANTS?

M ore and more people in the cultural West are shifting to a diet based primarily on plants. The health benefits and ecological sustainability of being powered by plants are often touted as some of the top reasons that people put down the knife and pick up the fork. But do more plants mean less politics? The answer is a resounding no.

Plant-Based Diets

- More and more people, young adults in particular, are shifting to a plant-based diet for both ethical and political reasons. They are opting to become vegan, vegetarian, or flexitarian.

  - A flexitarian eats a diet that is primarily plant based with the occasional meat product.

  - A vegan is a person who doesn't eat any animal products; this includes meat, eggs, and dairy. Many vegans also avoid eating honey, which is essentially regurgitated nectar from bees.

  - A vegetarian is a person who does not eat meat but may or may not eat dairy and eggs. A lacto-ovo vegetarian, the most common type, eats both. A lactovegetarian eats dairy but no eggs, and an ovovegetarian eats eggs but no dairy.

- Most estimates of how many vegetarians there are in the Unites States suggest that it's about 3% of the American population, or about 7 million people. Of this total, about 1 million practice veganism.

- Friends of the Earth International, a federation of autonomous environmental organizations around the world, estimates that there are about 375 million vegetarians worldwide. In the United States, many vegetarians select the diet based on ecological or cultural variables, such as environmental sustainability or empathy for animal welfare.

- There are many other reasons why people around the world are vegetarian. In some instances, it is not by choice. People who would happily consume meat, which offers an easily digestible source of good protein, do not have access to it.

- Some vegetarians make the choice to move to a plant-based diet because of the environmental impact of livestock production. Some adopt a meatless diet due to health concerns, citing the negative health outcomes and risks associated with consuming red meat in particular.

- Others make the move to a meatless diet based on ethical choices about the treatment and consumption of animals. Still others extend the no-harm principle to plants. One branch of veganism is called fruitarianism.

- Fruitarians are people who consume a diet that is almost exclusively composed of fruits. Within this category, there are several distinctions. Some people who eat fruits for more than 75% of their diet consider themselves to be fruitarian. Some eat only fruit that has already fallen off of the tree or vine.

- Some eat nuts and seeds, whereas others do not, arguing that seeds contain future plants or nuts or seeds. Those that only eat fruits that have fallen are called ahimsa fruitarians, and their aim is to eat a diet that does not kill anything, including plants.

- Nutritionists warn, however, that this form of veganism is the one that is most associated with nutritional deficiencies, likely because fruit-based diets are low in protein and iron as well as other micronutrients and fatty acids.

- There is an additional reason that people move to plant-based nourishment. For some, their diet is part of their religious practice. For Buddhism and Hinduism, a vegetarian diet is not mandated, but for Jainism, it is.

- Today, there is a cultural move throughout the United States to adopt a vegetarian diet. One of these movements is called forks over knives. It was originally based on a documentary film and became a movement advocating a low-fat, whole-food, plant-based diet as a means to avoid or reverse chronic degenerative diseases.

Moving from Farms to Cities

- Many people are opting for plants, particularly in the postindustrialized West, based on unsustainable meat-production practices. These practices are radically different from those that defined the domestication of animals 10,000 years ago.

- Our history, up until very recently, was a history that involved living in close proximity to the livestock and crops that nourished us. But this is changing drastically. Around the year 1900, about 40% of the U.S. population was made up of farmers. Today, that number is less than 1%—and is only expected to drop.

- The demographics of who is farming in the United States have also been changing over the past few decades. Compared to the agricultural census data from the early 2000s, the 2012 report showed an increase in the ethnic diversity of our country's farmers. However, the participation of women and young people is declining. There are also fewer new farms cropping up.

- Another downward trend is the amount of income that is generated by the farms. About 75% of farm operators generated less than $50,000 in agricultural products, and about 57% had sales less than $10,000. There's also an increase in the number of farmers who are making the majority of their household income off of the farm.

- And this isn't just in the United States. People all around the world are moving away from farms and into cities. The International Organization for Migration, which is related to the United Nations, published a world migration report in 2015 that outlined the general trends in migration that are characterizing current patterns of global movement.

- Global cities, such as London, New York, Tokyo, and Hong Kong, are still a major draw for most migrants. There has been much research exploring the effects of such a mass migration to cities, how swelling urban populations will have an effect on the environment, and how their demands for goods and services will be met. But much less has been made of the unsustainable population loss from the world's rural areas.

- If everyone moves to the cities, nobody is left to farm the land. Some farmers, such as those in the United States, use modern techniques, meaning that they need less labor to grow their crops. Even so, we're losing farmers—and we have no new farms.

- Most of the world's rural population is choosing to move to the city because decreasing rainfall and poor soils continue to keep productivity low. This means that an income from farming is unable to compete with better economic opportunities in cities.

- Despite the growing concern about what might happen to the food supply, many organizations are being proactive with the land left behind. The Society for Ecological Restoration, for example, is an international organization whose goal is to repair and recover degraded ecosystems, including effects from agriculture. They strive to ensure that their conservation efforts work to benefit the landowner as well as the environment.

- These programs are increasing, but a compounding issue is that the land that is still being used for agriculture needs to be viable. There is a multipronged effort to restore damaged agricultural lands that have been abandoned and to ensure that current agricultural lands are not only productive but sustainable.

Reducing Food Waste

- Another recommendation that aids in the creation of a more sustainable agricultural system is to simply reduce food waste. The Food and Agriculture Organization of the United Nations argues that the world throws away almost 3 trillion pounds of food per year.

- According to Oxfam International, a confederation of charitable organizations focused on alleviating global poverty, this amounts to more than enough food to feed every hungry person on the planet. This amount equates to about 1/3 of the world's food production, and it gets squandered for different reasons in different economies.

- In the developing world, much of this food is lost due to inadequate storage facilities, lack of refrigeration, and poor infrastructure, such as good-quality roads for transport.

- In the postindustrialized West, the issues arise when retailers do not purchase produce that is aesthetically appealing, meaning that it simply gets thrown away before it even gets loaded onto trucks to sell.

- In addition, retailers often buy and produce more food than they sell and serve, so much of it ends up in the trash. This also happens at the level of the individual household, where people throw away massive amounts of food each year.

- Beyond the actual food, there is associated squandering of resources that went into growing or producing the foods that are being thrown away. The virtual carbon footprint of our food, including water, is incredibly large. Simply growing the crops to either feed the animals that we eat or the plants that we directly consume takes immense amounts of water.

- The U.S. Environmental Protection Agency has some easy-to follow-guidelines for us to reduce waste.

    ○ Make lists of what meals you plan to prepare in a week and what ingredients you need to do so.

    ○ Properly store your fruits and vegetables so that they last longer. Freeze or can any surplus.

    ○ Get to know your freezer better. Many foods can be frozen and thawed, such as bread, sliced fruit, and meat.

    ○ Prepare and freeze perishable items so that they can be eaten later in the month.

    ○ Have a leftovers dinner night at your house each week.

    ○ Ask about portion sizes when out at restaurants. If you know you can't finish what they serve, either ask for less or take the leftovers home.

- Different organizations have other ways to reduce waste, such as keeping track of the amount of food that your family throws away. Simply recording it helps you realize how much you are actually tossing out.

- You can also try composting. According to the *Farmers' Almanac*, composting is a way of recycling naturally decomposing matter, almost always plant material. Meat, dairy, fish, and fat are generally not composted, but you can include coffee grounds, loose tea or compostable tea bags, eggshells and nutshells, pasta, dry goods, and shredded paper or newspaper.

The Politics of Plants

- Plants, which many turn to in order to avoid the politics of meat, carry their own history and political agenda. In addition to the environmental costs of growing enough crops to feed the expanding global population, there is much controversy surrounding the organic foods movement and the use of genetically modified organisms.

- Some people who purchase organic plant foods do so because they believe that it is healthier, is ecofriendly, or tastes better.

- The way that the industry determines which foods are organic is based on the way that the foods are grown and produced. Organic farming practices are meant to encourage water and soil conservation as well as reduce pollution by using natural fertilizers and crop rotation.

- It can be tricky, however, for the consumer to figure out the different types of classifications for organic foods. Any product that is listed as "organic" must be labeled by the U.S. Department of Agriculture. Products that are labeled as "100% organic" must contain only organically produced ingredients and processing aids.

- Products that are labeled "organic" must contain 95% organically produced ingredients and processing aids. Products that contain at least 70% organic ingredients are permitted to use the phrase "made with organic ingredients."

- Organic food is a multibillion-dollar industry that is growing all the time. Medical researchers have been working for decades to determine whether going organic actually confers any health benefits. The majority of the data suggests that it doesn't.

- While organic is unlikely to be more nutritious, people might choose to go organic for different reasons, including wanting to eat foods that are not treated with pesticides or food additives or for the decreased environmental impact of organic farming. While these foods are more expensive and tend to spoil faster, they do meet all of the safety standards of their nonorganic counterparts.

- Another politically charged issue associated with plant foods is the use of genetically modified organisms. The process involves extracting the DNA from one species and artificially placing it into the genes of a different plant or animal.

- Genetically engineered crops typically contain genes from bacteria that make them more resistant to pests or, conversely, more tolerant of herbicides. This allows the farmers to spray herbicides and not damage the crop.

- Other types of modifications include adding genes that stop apples from turning brown or adding genes to potatoes that reduce a potential cancerous chemical in the food that occurs when they're fried.

- Both of these crops were approved in the United States in 2014. Some states, such as Vermont, now require any genetically engineered foods to be labeled as such.

- Advocates of genetically engineered foods claim that the genetic changes help farmers use fewer pesticides and feed the world's growing population. Critics claim that they might actually increase herbicide- and pesticide-resistant weeds and insects.

Suggested Reading

Bloom, *American Wasteland*.
Gollner, *The Fruit Hunters*.
Pollan, *In Defense of Food*.

Questions

1. What are some of the ways in which the United Nations is working to restore damaged agricultural lands and make plant production more sustainable?

2. What are a few ways in which we can reduce the virtual carbon footprint of the food that we eat?

LECTURE
36

THE FUTURE OF FOOD

This final lecture is about the future of food. You will learn about changes in agriculture, both what is produced and how it is produced. You will also learn about changes in the way that animals are grown and fished for our consumption. Finally, you will discover how the evolutionary and cultural history of food can inform our present.

Progress in the Agricultural Industry

- There are many complicated and competing issues regarding the politics of plants that the world's leaders are currently grappling with. The United Nations has identified 3 issues that it sees as the most critical to achieve a sustainable nutritional future: environmental impact, feeding a growing population, and reducing poverty.

- The first issue is that the way in which crops are currently grown is not ecologically sustainable. The United Nations Environment Programme reported in 2010 that approximately 37% of Earth's landmass, minus Antarctica, is devoted to crops. The management of these crops uses about 70% of the world's freshwater withdrawal and is responsible for about 24% of the world's greenhouse gas emissions.

- Increased water use and rising temperatures are anticipated to increase water stress in many areas within the coming decades. And agriculture will remain an engine of growth, as having more people on the planet means having more people to feed.

- The second critical issue is the so-called food gap. While many aid organizations point out that right now we do technically grow enough to feed everyone on the planet, that isn't precisely accurate. We cannot simply redistribute crops.

- The basic point made by demographers and food scientists is that as the population grows, so does demand. It's not a fixed system. The food gap, then, is the estimated gap in production between the amount of food that the world is projected to need and the amount that it is projected to be able to produce.

- The current estimates by the World Resources Institute suggest that by 2050, the world will need about 69% more food than it produced in 2006. To close this gap, experts say that we need to empower the world's farmers, particularly its poorest ones who live in the developing world and lack access to resources and many sustainable practices.

- Addressing all of these issues has proven to be immensely difficult, as there are many competing interests, and coming up with global solutions is impossible in the short term. However, we are making strides. And the United Nations provides recommendations in each of these areas.

- New agricultural and food-production techniques will reduce the environmental impact of the agricultural industry. Some examples of ways in which this is occurring include agroforestry, changes in pesticide use, and modifications to livestock feed and animal waste products.

- Agroforestry is a farming system where trees and shrubs are integrated into farming and animal systems. The U.S Department of Agriculture recognizes 5 different types of systems.

  1. Alley cropping is when crops are planted simultaneously with long-term growth trees. This is good for the farmer, as it provides diversity of income as the tree crop matures. It also benefits the environment by improving land in areas where erosion has led to low production.

2. Forest farming or multistory cropping is a system in which crops are grown under a forest canopy.

3. Silvopasture is livestock grazing combined with forestry. This is a particularly good system for Christmas trees, conifers, timber, and even some fruit and nut orchards.

4. The use of windbreaks involves the linear planting of trees and shrubs that act to protect crops or livestock.

5. Riparian forest buffers are trees, shrubs, or grasses that are planted along a wood or a stream. Such forest buffers can improve wildlife habitats as well as trout streams.

- In addition to agroforestry, changes in pesticide use is another way that agriculture is becoming more sustainable. There has been a move toward reducing pesticide use in general, making better use of naturally occurring pest control, and pesticide management, such as managing dose, improving scheduling, and increasing regulatory control.

- Some countries have managed in the last few decades to successfully reduce their pesticide use by 50%. One of these countries is Denmark. Their action plan was originally initiated in 1986 to greatly reduce pesticide to protect the environment and safeguard human health. It was not an overnight fix, but the FAO points out that it has been quite successful, which is a hopeful sign that these methods can work on a large scale.

- Another fascinating practice is called vertical farming, which involves producing crops in stacked layers indoors in multistoried buildings or shipping containers. The practice is argued by ecologists to be better for the environment.

- It allows for food to be grown in urban centers, which is important, as the United Nations estimates that more than half of the world's population now lives in cities and suburbs. It also may require less embodied energy (the total energy that is used to produce a resource, from manufacture to transport to delivery) and produce less pollution than outdoor growing systems.

- Advocates claim that one way to ensure that vertical farms are, indeed, more energy efficient is to have them run on renewable energy, using solar panels or wind turbines.

- Vertical farms housed in stackable shipping containers are also beginning to be used. One company, called Freight Farms, sells ready-to-go containers that are equipped with climate technology and growing equipment. They cater to small businesses that want to produce food for the farm-to-table movement, a social movement that advocates serving local food in restaurants and schools that is directly acquired from the producer.

- Freight Farms makes this movement much easier in an urban setting. If the vertical-agriculture movement takes off, then it's possible that some restaurants can have their own farm on site—in a shipping container in the parking lot behind the restaurant.

Progress in the Livestock Industry

- Many strides are also being made in the livestock industry. New types of livestock feed are being introduced that can potentially reduce greenhouse gas emissions.

- According to the Food and Agriculture Organization of the United Nations, livestock contribute almost 15% of all anthropogenic, or human-made, greenhouse gases. There has been a move toward finding ways to reduce these emissions by using more sustainable feed, such as seaweed, distiller's grains or brewer's grains (the leftover solid residue from making beer), and sugarcane.

- Another way in which livestock production is working to reduce methane emissions is by genetic selection in the cattle themselves. In addition to the animals' diet and resident gut flora, genetics may also play a role in how much methane cows produce. Researchers are currently working on breeding cattle that would produce less gas.

- The end product of digestion, manure, is also being used to help curb the gas problem. Some farmers are experimenting with biogas digesters. It's a waste conversion system, typically a concrete container, that takes cow dung and turns it into nutrient-rich fertilizer, which can then be converted into energy.

- The dung is collected and piped into an engine that spins a generator and then creates electricity, which can be used to power their farms or sold back to the power grid. This so-called cow power can add up to a lot because every adult cow produces an estimated 30 gallons of manure per day.

Reducing the Food Gap

- Beyond innovative ways to reduce the environmental impact of agriculture and livestock, there are also ways that the world is working to reduce the food gap, one of the other major concerns of the United Nations.

- The use of biofortified crops is one of these attempts to address the global food crisis. This is a very controversial issue—and one that often divides environmental groups and human advocacy groups fighting world hunger. Biofortification is when the nutritional quality of crops is improved by either conventional plant breeding or through the use of modern biotechnology.

- This biotechnology often involves the use of genetically modified organisms (GMOs). Also called transgenic modification, this process involves extracting the DNA from one species and artificially placing it into the genes of a different plant or animal.

- The World Health Organization (WHO), lists a few examples of biofortified crops. These include iron-biofortified rice, beans, sweet potato, cassava, and legumes; zinc-biofortified wheat, rice, beans, sweet potato, and maize; provitamin A carotenoid–biofortified sweet potato, maize, and cassava; and amino acid–biofortified and protein-biofortified sourghum and cassava. These types of foods have the potential to greatly reduce micronutrient deficiencies around the world.

- Many people in the United States eat fortified foods every day. All that most of us have to do is walk to our pantry and pull out a breakfast cereal box. If you turn it over, the label will tell you that it's fortified with all kinds of micronutrients. Vitamin D milk and iodized salt are 2 additional examples.

- In every one of these foods, the motivation to fortify was made as a direct attempt to curb micronutrient deficiencies in the United States. These programs, which exist all over the cultural West, have been incredibly successful. The same types of fortification processes are not available in the developing world.

- Much of the debate on the use of GMOs centers on whether they are safe for the environment and for human consumption. We have good evidence to suggest that they do help curb micronutrient deficiencies, which is no small matter.

- We also have evidence, thus far, that they appear to be safe for human consumption. There is no actual medical evidence that they cause cancer, a fear voiced by many critics of GMOs. Despite this, many people do not want to eat foods containing any transgenic components.

- In the United States, as of 2017, the only way to ensure that none of your food contains any GMOs is to grow it all yourself, eat only organic produce, or live in Connecticut, Maine, or Vermont. While several U.S. states have introduced some type of legislation mandating that the use of GMOs must be labeled on the food, only these 3 have passed the mandates.

- Many say that this might be the beginning of a sea change and that many more states will start requiring foods containing GMOs to be labeled. One of the reasons that there is so much opposition to transgenic foods is that we don't know what long-term effects this process might have on the genetic diversity of our current non-GMO plants.

- There is nothing to suggest, as yet, that the process will have a negative outcome, but we simply don't have enough data to definitively say one way or the other. And while all of the research that has been done on the health effects of eating transgenic foods suggests that it's safe, we don't yet know the long-term effects.

- GMOs remain very controversial, as the process of genetically engineering foods could potentially work to meet the United Nation's goal of eliminating the food gap. The global population is growing, and it will need to be fed. To address systemic malnutrition and hunger around the world, many human rights organizations support the use of GMOs for biofortification.

- Another food that has been genetically engineered that people are resistant to is so-called test-tube meat, which also goes by the monikers in vitro meat, cruelty-free meat, and victimless meat. It is meat that has been grown with the help of tissue engineering in a test tube or in a 3-D printer.

- Cultured meat is argued by its supporters to be better for the environment, as it uses much fewer resources and does not produce greenhouse gases. It is also argued to be a potentially key food for helping to end the global hunger crisis. About 700 million people in the world are undernourished, and for those suffering from protein-energy malnutrition, this could alleviate much of the problem.

- Bioethicists argue that an additional benefit of artificial meat is that it stops cruelty to animals, and animal rights activists are excited about this prospect.

Suggested Reading

Despommier, *The Vertical Farm*.
Pollan, *In Defense of Food*.
Reiley, "Farm to Fable."

Questions

1. What is the so-called food gap, and how does the United Nations suggest that we address it?

2. How might vertical farming change the ways in which we produce plant food?

BIBLIOGRAPHY

Aiello, Leslie C., and Peter Wheeler. "The Expensive-Tissue Hypothesis: The Brain and the Digestive System in Human and Primate Evolution." *Current Anthropology* 36, no. 2 (1995): 199–221. Journal article that hypothesizes that because the brain is metabolically expensive, its growth and expansion in our evolutionary past must have been compensated for by a reduction in other expensive organs, particularly the digestive tract.

Alba-Lois, Luisa, and Claudia Segal-Kischinevzky. "Yeast Fermentation and the Making of Beer and Wine." *Nature Education* 3, no. 9 (2010): 17. Brief history of beer and wine production written for a general-science audience with special attention paid to the biological mechanisms behind alcohol production, namely yeast.

Armelagos, George J., and Mark Nathan Cohen, eds. *Paleopathology at the Origins of Agriculture*. Academic Press, 1984. Seminal edited volume that remains a landmark contribution to the field of anthropology today that outlines how the origins of agriculture map onto the first epidemiological transition.

Beeler, Selby B., and G. Brian Karas. *Throw Your Tooth on the Roof: Tooth Traditions from around the World*. Houghton Mifflin Harcourt, 2001. A children's book that documents the rich cultural traditions of what children around the world do when they lose a tooth.

Benyshek, Daniel C. "The 'Early Life' Origins of Obesity-Related Health Disorders: New Discoveries regarding the Intergenerational Transmission of Developmentally Programmed Traits in the Global Cardiometabolic Health Crisis." *American Journal of Physical Anthropology* 152, no. S57 (2013): 79–93. A wide-ranging academic review article that chronicles the causes of the current global obesity pandemic. Specifically focuses on the ways in which the field of developmental origins of health and disease influences our understanding of how developmental programming is intricately tied to current patterns of cardiometabolic diseases.

Blake, Michael. *Maize for the Gods: Unearthing the 9,000-year History of Corn*. University of California Press, 2015. Traces the history of maize from its first domestication to the ways in which it has been tied to history and culture for the past 10,000 years. Includes perspectives and data from anthropologists, archaeologists, archaeobotanists, and plant geneticists.

Bloom, Jonathan. *American Wasteland: How America Throws Away Nearly Half of Its Food (And What We Can Do about It)*. Da Capo Press, 2011. Explores the food-waste epidemic in the United States and offers guidelines for how to reduce waste in your own home.

Bone, Eugenia. *Mycophilia: Revelations from the Weird World of Mushrooms*. Rodale, 2011. Written for a general audience by a food writer and cookbook author, this book examines mushrooms, both as a hallucinogen and a culinary delicacy.

Bostwick, William. *The Brewer's Tale: A History of the World according to Beer*. W. W. Norton & Company, 2014. Rich and detailed history of brewing, beginning with mead and following 5000 years of fermentation. Winner of the 2014 U.S. Gourmand Drinks Award, the book chronicles and recreates beers of the past.

Bradbury, Joanne. "Docosahexaenoic Acid (DHA): An Ancient Nutrient for the Modern Human Brain." *Nutrients* 3, no. 5 (2011): 529–554. An easily accessible paper that reviews the unique role that DHA plays in neurodevelopment and the prevention of neuropsychiatric and neurodegenerative disorders and in human evolution.

Braun, Stephen. *Buzz: The Science and Lore of Alcohol and Caffeine*. Oxford University Press, 1996. History of beer and coffee that specifically addresses alcohol and caffeine addiction.

Buchmann, Christine, Sarah Prehsler, Anna Hartl, and Christian R. Vogl. "The Importance of Baobab (*Adansonia digitata L.*) in Rural West African Subsistence: Suggestion of a Cautionary Approach to International Market Export of Baobab Fruits." *Ecology of Food and Nutrition* 49, no. 3 (2010): 145–172. Reviews the cultural significance of baobab trees and their fruits and discusses the ways in which increased export of the fruits has the potential to negatively influence livelihoods and nutritional status.

Cadbury, Deborah. *Chocolate Wars: The 150-Year Rivalry between the World's Greatest Chocolate Makers*. PublicAffairs, 2011. Written for a general audience by a member of the famous family of chocolatiers, the Cadburys, this is a rich and fascinating accounting of the 150-year business rivalries that characterize the race for the best, and most popular, chocolate bar

Campbell, T. Colin, and Caldwell B. Esselstyn. *Forks over Knives: The Plant-Based Way to Health*. Edited by Gene Stone. Workman Publishing, 2011. A controversial diet plan—that became a cultural movement—that proposes that a plant-based diet can reduce risk of disease. Based on the documentary of the same name.

Cochran, Gregory, and Henry Harpending. *The 10,000 Year Explosion: How Civilization Accelerated Human Evolution*. Basic Books, 2009. A crossover book written by 2 scholars, this book argues that human genetics have changed and will continue to change much more rapidly than scientists have previously believed. Also discusses the link between genetic change and cultural change.

Cockrall-King, Jennifer. *Food and the City: Urban Agriculture and the New Food Revolution*. Prometheus Books, 2012. Chronicles alternative urban food systems and how they are becoming a social movement that is pivoted against industrial-produced agriculture.

Coe, Sophie D., Michael D. Coe, and Ryan J. Huxtable. *The True History of Chocolate*. Thames and Hudson, 1996. Tells the rich story of chocolate, written for a public audience using data from archaeology, botany, and culinary history.

Cohen, Rich. "Sugar Love (A Not So Sweet Story)." *National Geographic* 224, no. 2 (2013): 78–97. A brief history of sugar, how our bodies process it, and how it is related to the obesity pandemic and other metabolic diseases.

Cordain, Loren. *The Paleo Diet Revised: Lose Weight and Get Healthy by Eating the Foods You Were Designed to Eat.* 3rd ed. Houghton Mifflin Harcourt, 2010. Written by an expert on the Paleo diet, this revised edition of the best-selling guide offers a nutrition program, recipes, and meal plans.

Crane, Ethel Eva. *The World History of Beekeeping and Honey Hunting.* 2nd ed. Routledge, 2013. Extensive and lively history of apiculture and the long and enduring relationship between humans and honey bees. Written by the former director of the International Bee Research Association and a world expert on bees.

Crittenden, Alyssa N. "The Importance of Honey Consumption in Human Evolution." *Food and Foodways* 19, no. 4 (2011): 257–273. Reviews the evidence of honey consumption in human evolution using analysis of rock art, data from nonhuman primate species, and diet composition of contemporary foraging populations around the world.

Cunnane, Stephen C. *Survival of the Fattest: The Key to Human Brain Evolution.* World Scientific, 2005. Written for a crossover academic audience by a fatty-acid researcher and nutritionist, this book argues that our species evolved to eat a shore-based diet that included shellfish, fish, and marsh plants and led to our ancestors obtaining necessary fatty acids for brain growth and maintenance.

Czarra, Fred. *Spices: A Global History.* Reaktion Books, 2009. A lively and thorough history of the spice trade written for a general audience with particular focus on 5 spices: pepper, chili pepper, cinnamon, nutmeg, and cloves.

Dalby, Andrew. *Dangerous Tastes: The Story of Spices*. California Studies in Food and Culture, book 1. University of California Press, 2000. A history of the relationship between the spice trade and world politics and geohistory. Written as a crossover academic book, this history of spices focuses on cinnamon, cloves, ginger, pepper, saffron, and chili.

Davis, Mike. *Planet of Slums*. Verso, 2006. Riveting exploration of the world's slums that house an estimated population of 1 billion people.

De la Peña, Carolyn Thomas. *Empty Pleasures: The Story of Artificial Sweeteners from Saccharin to Splenda*. University of North Carolina Press, 2010. The history of artificial sweeteners written for a crossover science audience.

de Montellano, Bernard Ortiz. *Aztec Medicine, Health, and Nutrition*. Rutgers University Press, 1990. An academic text chronicling the history of food and medicine in ancient Aztec culture.

Despommier, Dickson. *The Vertical Farm: Feeding the World in the 21st Century*. Macmillan, 2010. Written by a retired professor from Colombia University, and one of the world's undisputed leaders in vertical-farm technology, this book introduces the concept of vertical agriculture and then outlines how it can be used to feed the world.

Diamond, Jared. *Guns, Germs, and Steel: The Fates of Human Societies*. W. W. Norton, 1997. Winner of the 1998 Pulitzer Prize for General Nonfiction, this book explores how Europeans obtained the so-called ingredients of power (guns, germs, and steel) that allowed them to expand around the world.

Donovan, Tristan. *Fizz: How Soda Shook Up the World*. Chicago Review Press, 2013. Written for a general audience, this book provides a social, cultural, and culinary history of cola beverages.

Eaton, S. Boyd, Marjorie Shostak, and Melvin Konner. *The Paleolithic Prescription: A Program of Diet & Exercise and a Design for Living*.

HarperCollins Publishers, 1988. One of the first manuscripts suggesting that our bodies are an evolutionary mismatch with our modern environment. The thrust of the book is that we adapted in very different ecological and nutritional circumstances from which we now live and that if we attempted to modify our diet and lifestyle to more clearly reflect our Paleolithic past, we would be much healthier.

Feldman, David. *Water*. Polity, 2012. An overview of the geopolitics of water that explores the complexity of future challenges in distribution and conservation. Written for a general audience.

Fiorenza, Luca, Stefano Benazzi, Amanda G. Henry, Domingo C. Salazar-García, Ruth Blasco, Andrea Picin, Stephen Wroe, and Ottmar Kullmer. "To Meat or Not to Meat? New Perspectives on Neanderthal Ecology." *American Journal of Physical Anthropology* 156, no. S59 (2015): 43–71. Challenges the assumption that Neanderthals were exclusively meat eaters by presenting data from lithic and zooarchaeological analyses, stable isotopic analysis, paleopathology, tooth-wear studies, and the use of dental calculus for reconstructing diet composition.

Fishman, Charles. *The Big Thirst: The Secret Life and Turbulent Future of Water*. Simon and Schuster, 2012. Fascinating treatise on water, in all of its forms. Traces the beginning of water on Earth all the way until the 21st century, when water is a commodity and a highly valuable resource with its own turbulent geopolitical identity. Written for a popular audience, this thorough examination of water ends with ways in which conservation is possible, on both the national and global level.

Food and Agriculture Organization of the United Nations. "Food Loss and Food Waste." http://www.fao.org/food-loss-and-food-waste/en/. Quantifies current estimates of food loss and waste around the world and outlines global aims to reduce such waste.

Funderburg, Anne Cooper. *Sundae Best: A History of Soda Fountains*. Popular Press, 2002. History of the soda fountain in the United States and how it mapped onto the rise of the suburban revolution.

Frink, Liam, and Celeste Giordano. "Women and Subsistence Food Technology: The Arctic Seal Poke Storage System." *Food and Foodways* 23, no. 4 (2015): 251–272. A study of the pan-Arctic seal poke system, which is an entire seal skin turned into a leak-proof container. The analysis of this storage system highlights food-processing methods in circumpolar regions and underscores the importance of women's processing behaviors.

Fung, Brian. "The World's Oldest Dental Filling Was Made of Ceeswax." *The Atlantic.* https://www.theatlantic.com/health/archive/2012/09/the-worlds-oldest-dental-filling-was-made-of-beeswax/262635/. Reviews the discovery of a 6500-year-old piece of beeswax and how this informs our understanding of ancient dental practices.

Fussell, Betty Harper. *The Story of Corn.* University of New Mexico Press, 1992. The history of corn, with an emphasis on corn in the Americas, that explores the plant as food, fetish, and commodity.

Gentilcore, David. *Pomodoro! A History of the Tomato in Italy.* Columbia University Press, 2010. Reviews the history of the tomato with particular discussion on how it became a symbol of national identity in Italy.

Gibbons, Ann. "The Evolution of Diet." *National Geographic.* http://www.nationalgeographic.com/foodfeatures/evolution-of-diet/#. A thorough overview of major concepts in the study of the evolution of human nutrition with examples from contemporary foraging populations all around the world.

Gilman, Sander L. *Fat: A Cultural History of Obesity.* Polity, 2008. Written for a crossover scientific audience, this book does a clear job of tracing public concern of obesity from the mid-19th century to today, with specific emphasis on the history of fat in culture and identity.

Gluckman, Peter, and Mark Hanson. *Mismatch: Why Our World No Longer Fits Our Bodies.* Oxford University Press, 2006. Written by 2 medical scientists, this crossover book pulls from many different disciplines, including anthropology, medicine, and developmental science, to explore developmental origins of health and disease and how our prenatal environment forecasts our future environment.

Gollner, Adam Leith. *The Fruit Hunters: A Story of Nature, Adventure, Commerce, and Obsession*. Simon and Schuster, 2013. Fascinating popular-science book that chronicles the history of the fruits that we eat and how they are tethered to history.

Goode, Jamie. *I Taste Red: The Science of Tasting Wine*. University of California Press, 2016. Written for an academic or academic crossover audience, this fascinating book uses data from the body's sensory system and the fields of psychology, philosophy, and flavor chemistry to detail how we perceive and enjoy wine—from a historical and biological perspective.

Goren-Inbar, Naama, Nira Alperson, Mordechai E. Kislev, Orit Simchoni, Yoel Melamed, Adi Ben-Nun, and Ella Werker. "Evidence of Hominin Control of Fire at Gesher Benot Ya'aqov, Israel." *Science* 304, no. 5671 (2004): 725–727. Presents data from the discovery of burned seeds, wood, and flint at the archaeological site of Gesher Benot Ya'aqov in Israel that provides evidence that foods such as olive, wild barley, and wild grape were roasted.

Gremillion, Kristen J. *Ancestral Appetites: Food in Prehistory*. Cambridge University Press, 2011. Short review of the history of the human diet, with special emphasis on archaeological data.

Gustavsson, Jenny, Christel Cederberg, Ulf Sonesson, Robert Van Otterdijk, and Alexandre Meybeck. "Global Food Losses and Food Waste: Extent, Causes and Prevention." Food and Agriculture Organization of the United Nations, 2011. Technical report from the Swedish Institute for Food and Biotechnology on patterns of global food loss and food waste.

Hanson, Thor. *The Triumph of Seeds: How Grains, Nuts, Kernels, Pulses, and Pips Conquered the Plant Kingdom and Shaped Human History*. Basic Books, 2016. A historical overview of the history of seeds, including origins of particular seeds and pulses and their role in history.

Hardy, Karen. "Prehistoric String Theory: How Twisted Fibres Helped to Shape the World." *Antiquity* 82, no. 316 (2008): 271–280. Reviews the role of string in human evolution.

Harmand, Sonia, Jason E. Lewis, Craig S. Feibel, Christopher J. Lepre, Sandrine Prat, Arnaud Lenoble, and Xavier Boës, et al. "3.3-Million-Year-Old Stone Tools from Lomekwi 3, West Turkana, Kenya." *Nature* 521, no. 7552 (2015): 310–315. Reports the discovery of Lomekwi 3, a 3.3-million-year-old archaeological site in Kenya. The discovery of these tools pushed back the dates for the beginning of stone tools, as it predates Olduvai. As of 2017, these were the oldest stone tools recovered.

Hornsey, Ian Spencer. *A History of Beer and Brewing*. Royal Society of Chemistry, 2003. Written as a crossover book, this rich history of beer and the brewery process is scholarly yet accessible. Defines beer and chronicles the first beers.

Hrdy, Sarah Blaffer. *Mothers and Others*. 2nd ed. Harvard University Press, 2011. Impactful treatise in the field of evolutionary anthropology that proposes that humans evolved as cooperative breeders, where females of the species relied on the assistance of helpers, both genetic and nongenetic, to rear children in our evolutionary past.

Ingraham, John L. *Kin: How We Came to Know Our Microbe Relatives*. Harvard University Press, 2017. Written for an academic crossover audience by a microbiologist, this book chronicles our long relationship with microbes and how we came to understand our own microbe inheritance and the relatedness of all living organisms on Earth.

Jacob, Heinrich Eduard. *Six Thousand Years of Bread: Its Holy and Unholy History*. Skyhorse Publishing Inc., 2007. History of bread from ancient Egypt to today.

Kaptchuk, Ted. *The Web That Has No Weaver: Understanding Chinese Medicine*. BookBaby, 2014. Popular book that is argued to be a comprehensive guide to the theory and practice of Chinese alternative medicine.

Kelly, Robert L. *The Lifeways of Hunter-Gatherers: The Foraging Spectrum*. Cambridge University Press, 2013. An anthropological overview of contemporary foragers in the world, with information on demography, history, and ecology of each population covered.

King, Melanie. *Tea, Coffee, & Chocolate: How We Fell in Love with Caffeine*. Oxford University Press, 2015. A rich culinary history of tea, coffee, and chocolate—beverages that changed the world.

Kiple, Kenneth F., ed. *The Cambridge World History of Food*. Cambridge University Press, 2000. A comprehensive 2-volume encyclopedic-like history of food and cuisine.

Kittler, Pamela Goyan, Kathryn P. Sucher, and Marcia Nelms. *Food and Culture*. Cengage Learning, 2011. Textbook for the university level that is an introduction to the study of food and culture.

Koeppel, Dan. *Banana: The Fate of the Fruit That Changed the World*. Penguin, 2008. Details the history and cultural significance of the banana, ending with a discussion of how the banana is becoming endangered.

Kurlansky, Mark. *Salt*. Random House, 2011. A comprehensive history of salt written for a popular audience.

Letcher, Andy. *Shroom: A Cultural History of the Magic Mushroom*. Faber & Faber, 2006. Written for a popular audience, this lively exploration of the magic mushroom follows the history of hallucinogenic fungi around the world.

Marean, Curtis W. "When the Sea Saved Humanity." *Scientific American* 303, no. 2 (2010): 54–61. Reviews the data that suggests that between 195,000 and 123,000 years ago, the human population size plummeted due to cold, dry climate. Some paleodemographers, and the author of this paper, suggest that all people alive today are descendent from a coastal population who survived this climatic catastrophe in a single region.

Mark, Sara Haviva. "The Soda Ban Decision: What It Really Means." *Huffington Post*. http://www.huffingtonpost.com/news/new-york-soda-ban/. News article on the history and significance of the soda ban in New York in 2013.

Marlowe, Frank. *The Hadza: Hunter-Gatherers of Tanzania*. Origins of Human Behavior and Culture, vol. 3. University of California Press, 2010. An ethnography of the Hadza foragers of Tanzania from an evolutionary anthropological and behavioral ecological perspective.

Martin, Laura C. *Tea: The Drink That Changed the World*. Tuttle Publishing, 2011. A comprehensive world history of tea written for a general audience.

Mayo Clinic. "Obesity." http://www.mayoclinic.org/diseases-conditions/obesity/basics/definition/con-20014834. Offers easy-to-understand definition, symptoms, and causes of obesity.

McGovern, Patrick E. *Ancient Wine: The Search for the Origins of Viniculture*. Princeton University Press, 2013. Comprehensive history of viniculture (wine making), beginning with the hypothesis that early human ancestors stumbled upon wine accidentally in the wild, written for an academic or academic crossover audience.

———. *Uncorking the Past: The Quest for Wine, Beer, and Other Alcoholic Beverages*. University of California Press, 2009. Written for a crossover audience by an academic who is also known as the "Indiana Jones of ancient ales, wines, and extreme beverages," this book provides a rich history of ancient alcoholic beverages from all around the world.

McKenna, Terence. *Food of the Gods: The Search for the Original Tree of Knowledge—A Radical History of Plants, Drugs and Human Evolution*. Random House, 1999. Written by an ethnobotanist, this book provides a rich history of the politics of tobacco, tea, coffee, opium, and alcohol. Highlights the often-gray boundaries between food and drugs (both medicinal and hallucinogenic).

McQuaid, John. *Tasty: The Art and Science of What We Eat*. Simon and Schuster, 2016. Written for a popular-science audience, this fascinating book explores the biology behind the science of taste.

Menzel, Peter, and Faith D'Aluisio. *Hungry Planet: What the World Eats*. Material World Press, 2005. Offers detailed descriptions and photographs of the weekly diet of 30 families from around the world.

———. *What I Eat: Around the World in 80 Diets*. Ten Speed, 2011. A photographic collection of the daily diets of 80 people from around the world coupled with essays and demographic information on the featured people and their diets.

Mintz, Sidney Wilfred. *Sweetness and Power*. New York: Viking, 1985. Comprehensive history of the ways in which sugar played a vital role in world history and was tethered to colonial slavery and the machine era.

Morán, Elizabeth. *Sacred Consumption: Food and Ritual in Aztec Art and Culture*. University of Texas Press, 2016. Examination of the significance of ritual and food in ancient Aztec art.

Neu, Frank. "We May Be Sitting Ourselves to Death." *The Atlantic*, 1961. https://www.theatlantic.com/magazine/archive/1961/11/we-may-be-sitting-ourselves-to-death/306504/. From the 1960s and written by the then-spokesman for the American Dairy Association, this article is one of the first times that sedentism (reduced physical activity) was linked with increased obesity and cardiometabolic disease.

Noble, Louise. *Medicinal Cannibalism in Early Modern English Literature and Culture*. Springer, 2011. An academic text that explores the links between early modern literary representations of the consumed body and the consumption of corpses for medicinal purposes.

NOVA scienceNOW. "Lice and Human Evolution." PBS. http://www.pbs.org/wgbh/nova/evolution/lice.html. Popular-science article on how the DNA of lice tells us a lot about human evolution.

Oaklander, Mandy. "20 Delicious Bug Recipes from Chefs." *TIME*. http://time.com/3830167/eating-bugs-insects-recipes/. Twenty recipes provided by celebrity chefs that incorporate insects into the dishes.

Paul, Annie Murphy. *Origins: How the Nine Months before Birth Shape the Rest of Our Lives*. Simon and Schuster, 2010. Written for a general-science audience, this book introduces the field of fetal-origins research and explores the ways in which our first 9 months in utero influences us from infancy to adulthood.

Pendergrast, Mark. *Uncommon Grounds: The History of Coffee and How It Transformed Our World*. Basic Books, 2010. World history of coffee, from its first cultivation to the culinary obsession it is today.

Pollan, Michael. *In Defense of Food: An Eater's Manifesto*. Penguin, 2008. Building on his earlier book for the public, *The Omnivore's Dilemma*, in this book the author unpacks what we should eat and why. His conclusion is that we should, "Eat food. Not too much. Mostly plants."

—————. *The Omnivore's Dilemma: A Natural History of Four Meals*. Penguin, 2006. In this fascinating treatise on the current Western diet, the author traces 4 meals back to their roots to dissect and explore why we eat what we eat today and what it means for our evolutionary past and our biological future.

Pond, Wilson G., Buford L. Nichols, and Dan L. Brown, eds. *Adequate Food for All: Culture, Science, and Technology of Food in the 21st Century*. CRC Press, 2009. A comprehensive edited volume written for a crossover audience that focuses on the factors that threaten to compromise food production and distribution in the future.

Praeger, Dave. *Poop Culture: How America Is Shaped by Its Grossest National Product*. Feral House, 2007. Written for a popular-science audience, this book offers a history of the human fascination with poop, ranging from the history of sanitation and toilet paper to why people find bathroom humor so funny.

Pruetz, Jill D., and Paco Bertolani. "Savanna Chimpanzees, *Pan troglodytes verus*, Hunt with Tools." *Current Biology* 17, no. 5 (2007): 412–417. Documents the first report of chimpanzees in the wild using tools to assist with hunting of other vertebrate animals.

Reiley, Laura. "Farm to Fable." *Tampa Bay Times*. http://www.tampabay.com/projects/2016/food/farm-to-fable/. Investigative reporting on the farm-to-table movement in Tampa that uncovered the unsavory truth about the restaurants that claimed to be part of the movement.

Rook, Graham, ed. *The Hygiene Hypothesis and Darwinian Medicine.* Springer Science & Business Media, 2009. An academic edited volume that explores the hygiene hypothesis, which suggests that the reduced pattern of exposure to microorganisms in our evolutionary past has led to a disordered regulation of the immune system that has then led to increases in certain chronic inflammatory disorders.

Rose, Sarah. *For All the Tea in China: How England Stole the World's Favorite Drink and Changed History.* Penguin, 2010. A richly woven history of how the British East India Company acquired its tea crops from China—and, in so doing, changed world history.

Rubel, William. *Bread: A Global History.* Reaktion Books, 2011. Detailed history of bread, going as far back as almost 20,000 years. Written for a popular audience, this lively book combines culinary history, culture, and aspects of a cookbook.

Ryan, Órla. *Chocolate Nations: Living and Dying for Cocoa in West Africa.* Zed Books, 2011. History of the importance of cocoa production in West Africa that examines how cocoa, while one of the most valuable commodities in the world, provides a very limited income that is controlled by manufacturers, governments, and supermarkets.

Salaman, Redcliffe N., and William Glynn Burton. *The History and Social Influence of the Potato.* 2nd ed. Cambridge University Press, 1985.

First published in 1949, this book is still considered one of the most comprehensive compendia on the history of the potato.

Schatzker, Mark. *The Dorito Effect: The Surprising New Truth about Food and Flavor*. Simon and Schuster, 2015. History of food flavoring and our world's current quest to overcome blandness in food.

Scheper-Hughes, Nancy. *Death without Weeping: The Violence of Everyday Life in Brazil*. University of California Press, 1993. A riveting ethnography written by an anthropologist that chronicles the everyday-lived experience of scarcity and death among the women and children of a hillside favela (urban slum) in Brazil.

Schlosser, Eric. *Fast Food Nation: The Dark Side of the All-American Meal*. 2nd ed. Houghton Mifflin Harcourt, 2012. Rich history of the American fast-food industry and the health consequences of the shift to a fast-food diet.

Schnorr, Stephanie L., Marco Candela, Simone Rampelli, Manuela Centanni, Clarissa Consolandi, Giulia Basaglia, and Silvia Turroni, et al. "Gut Microbiome of the Hadza Hunter-Gatherers." *Nature Communications* 5 (2014). The first study of the gut microbiome among a foraging population that shows that the foragers have higher levels of microbial richness and biodiversity when compared to people living in the postindustrialized West.

Schutt, Bill. *Cannibalism: A Perfectly Natural History*. Algonquin Books, 2017. History of the practice of cannibalism in evolutionary terms and throughout cultural history.

Shepherd, Gordon M. *Neurogastronomy: How the Brain Creates Flavor and Why It Matters*. Columbia University Press, 2013. Written by a neuroscientist, this book explores the links between neural chemistry and taste.

Smith, Andrew F. *Eating History: Thirty Turning Points in the Making of American Cuisine*. Columbia University Press, 2009. Expertly written by a food historian, this book recounts how the American meal came to be.

Sonnenburg, Justin, and Erica Sonnenburg. *The Good Gut: Taking Control of Your Weight, Your Mood, and Your Long-Term Health.* Penguin, 2015. Written for a popular-science audience by 2 microbiologists, this book introduces us to microbiota and discusses how changes in our culture, such as overuse of broad-spectrum antibiotics and diet composition, have led to a mass extinction of critical bacteria in and on our bodies.

Standage, Tom. *A History of the World in 6 Glasses.* Bloomsbury Publishing USA, 2006. Traces the ways in which world history was influenced by 6 beverages: beer, wine, spirits, coffee, tea, and soda.

Stanford, Craig B. "Chimpanzee Hunting Behavior and Human Evolution." *American Scientist* 83, no. 3 (1995): 256–261. Reviews hunting behavior by wild chimpanzees and explores the significance of this predatory behavior for the evolution of human behavior.

Taubes, Gary. *The Case against Sugar.* Portobello Books, 2016. Explores America's history with sugar and the nutritional and health consequences of our love of the sweet stuff.

Taylor, Gerald, ed. *Turmeric: Nutritional Properties, Uses and Potential Benefits.* Nova Science Publishers Inc., 2015. An edited volume that reviews the clinical evidence that curcumin, the principal curcuminoid of the Indian spice turmeric, has health benefits. Includes clinical data up to 2015.

The Huffington Post. "Raw Look inside the Life of a Nepalese Honey Hunter." http://www.huffingtonpost.com/2014/03/11/honey-hunters-nepal_n_4937079.html. Photo essay on the Gurung honey hunters living in Nepal.

Ungar, Peter S. *Teeth: A Very Short Introduction.* Oxford University Press, 2014. An overview of the evolution of mammalian teeth with special discussion of how human teeth evolved.

United Nations. "Housing and Slum Upgrading." UN-Habitat. http://unhabitat.org/urban-themes/housing-slum-upgrading/. Outlines the UN's definition of an urban slum, highlighting what characterizes slums and the UN's Global Housing Strategy.

Varki, Ajit. "Uniquely Human Evolution of Sialic Acid Genetics and Biology." *Proceedings of the National Academy of Sciences* 107, no. Supplement 2 (2010): 8939–8946. Provides an introduction to how a genetic change in human evolution led to the inactivation of a gene called *CMAH*, which resulted in the loss of synthesis of the Sia *N*-glycolylneuraminic acid (Neu5Gc) and increase in expression of the precursor *N*-acetylneuraminic acid (Neu5Ac). There is still human metabolic incorporation of Neu5Gc from the consumption of animal foods.

Visser, Margaret. *The Rituals of Dinner: The Origins, Evolution, Eccentricities, and Meaning of Table Manners*. Open Road Media, 2015. History of the eating ritual throughout history and across the globe.

Waltner-Toews, David. *The Origin of Feces: What Excrement Tells Us about Evolution, Ecology, and a Sustainable Society*. ECW Press, 2013. Comprehensive book written for a general-science audience that discusses how integral feces is to agriculture, public health, biodiversity, food production, and global ecosystems—ranging from the history of flushing toilets to dung beetles.

World Business Council for Sustainable Development. "Water: Facts and Trends." http://www.unwater.org/downloads/Water_facts_and_trends.pdf. Brochure and UN working document that is publicly available, providing a general overview of consumption patterns and societal challenges in distribution of water.

Wenk, Gary L. *Your Brain on Food: How Chemicals Control Your Thoughts and Feelings*. Oxford University Press, 2014. Written for a popular audience, this book explores how what we eat has consequences for how we think, feel, and act.

Wiessner, Polly W. "Embers of Society: Firelight Talk among the Ju/'hoansi Bushmen." *Proceedings of the National Academy of Sciences* 111, no.

39 (2014): 14027–14035. Explores the significance of the evolution of tending fire for social interaction and storytelling using data from the Ju/'hoansi foragers.

Wild, Antony. *Coffee: A Dark History*. W. W. Norton & Company, 2005. History of the coffee-production industry with an emphasis on its colonial past and present situation, in which the majority of the world's coffee producers live in countries facing unemployment, mandatory migration, and social disruption.

Wilkins, Jayne, Benjamin J. Schoville, Kyle S. Brown, and Michael Chazan. "Evidence for Early Hafted Hunting Technology." *Science* 338, no. 6109 (2012): 942–946. Discussion of when hafted tools appear in the fossil record. Hafting technology allowed projectile points to be attached to a staff, which was an important step in the construction of weaponry of our ancestors.

Witzel, Michael Karl. *The American Drive-In: History and Folklore of the Drive-In Restaurant in American Car Culture. Motorbooks International*, 1994. A history of the American drive-in and how it was associated with the car culture and suburban lifestyle that also dominated during the era.

Wong, Kate. "The First Butchers." *Scientific American* 303, no. 4 (2010): 21–21. A popular-science article that reviews archaeological evidence of cut marks on animal bones dating to more than 3 million years ago at a site called Dikika.

Wood, Brian M., Herman Pontzer, David A. Raichlen, and Frank W. Marlowe. "Mutualism and Manipulation in Hadza–Honeyguide Interactions." *Evolution and Human Behavior* 35, no. 6 (2014): 540–546. Explores the relationship between Hadza hunters and the honeyguide bird (*Indicator indicator*). Proposes an alternative hypothesis that suggests that Hadza hunters aim to keep the birds hungry to solicit their assistance in locating bee hives.

Wrangham, Richard. *Catching Fire: How Cooking Made Us Human*. Basic Books, 2009. Explores the evidence for the evolution of the control of fire and cooking and proposes that thermal processing, or cooking, is what made us human.

Young, Sera. *Craving Earth: Understanding Pica—The Urge to Eat Clay, Starch, Ice, and Chalk*. Columbia University Press, 2011. Documents the history of nonfood cravings using historical, ethnographic, and biomedical data.

Young, Sharon M., and Daniel C. Benyshek. "In Search of Human Placentophagy: A Cross-Cultural Survey of Human Placenta Consumption, Disposal Practices, and Cultural Beliefs." *Ecology of Food and Nutrition* 49, no. 6 (2010): 467–484. Research article documenting the practice of maternal placentophagy (ingestion of the placenta postpartum) around the world.

Zimmerman, Jereme. *Make Mead Like a Viking: Traditional Techniques for Brewing Natural, Wild-Fermented, Honey-Based Wines and Beers*. Chelsea Green Publishing, 2015. Guide for home mead makers and packed with interesting facts.

IMAGE CREDITS

Page No.

NOTES

NOTES

NOTES

NOTES